W9-AFT-616

THE
DEPARTMENTAL LABORATORY
ASSISTANT
IN
BIOLOGICAL
SCIENCE

A BOOK OF PRINCIPLES,
METHODS AND TECHNIQUES

Harold C. Steele, Ed. D.
The University of Alabama in Huntsville

BRIAR CLIFF COLLEC
LIBRARY

SIOUX CITY, IOWA

DORRANCE & COMPANY
Philadelphia

Copyright © 1966 by Harold C. Steele
All Rights Reserved

Library of Congress Catalog Card Number: 66-29353
Manufactured in the United States of America

QH
315
.S78

For

Sherri, Montie, and Laura Dane

47609

To The Biology Teaching Staff

This volume represents a serious effort to professionalize the position of the biology assistant (often called laboratory assistant) and to show that the assistant can and should function as an integral part of the instructional staff of the department.

A fundamental purpose of the book is to relieve the department chairman and the permanent teaching staff of many problems associated with trained and untrained graduate and undergraduate assistants. This volume provides answers to numerous "what," "when," "where," "how," and "why" questions regarding general departmental and laboratory operations. Finding answers to such questions too often interrupts the schedules of permanent teaching staff members. This is a book of suggestions for the assistant. It is a volume of answers to his everyday problems.

The author believes that an assistant's mastery of this volume, coupled with discussions of problems during staff meetings and occasional personal conferences with the department chairman or other designated superior, will add greatly to the efficiency of routine departmental operation and will also help to create a much-needed professional image for the assistant.

To The Assistant

You have been honored by your appointment as a departmental laboratory assistant in the biological sciences. In that position you will be working closely throughout a quarter, semester, or year with a department chairman, a supervising laboratory director, or some other designated superior. You will also be in professional contact with numbers of students who are enrolled in the biology courses. You will be required to learn the mechanics of planning, organizing, arranging, conducting, and cleaning laboratories associated with various types of course experiences. While many of your tasks may be considered menial, your appointment as an assistant means that you are much more than an average student making his way through college under complete supervision. Your appointment will provide you with a continuing challenge to grow in professional experience. Your contacts with students and departmental teaching personnel should also contribute much to the development of your own personal philosophy of teaching and learning.

In order to obtain full benefit from your assistantship, you should endeavor on your own to become more literate in the biological sciences. You should try to strengthen your acquaintance with facts and methods and with the historical and contemporary problems of biology. You should be knowledgeable regarding the lives and contributions of renowned and little-known investigators. You should apply with students your information concerning the wealth of biological vocational opportunities. Students under your direction should be introduced to the excitement of biological research. Your assistantship in the departmental program should stimulate you to grow as a professional worker and to add your own progressive ideas and experiences toward improving the departmental philosophy and operation. This volume is designed to help you achieve such status.

While fulfilling your responsibilities with the help of this book, you should keep constantly in mind those qualities of enthusiasm and independence, maturity of judgment, dependability in conducting assignments, and a receptive willingness to learn and to profit from various criticisms of your work that will be offered by your supervisors.

CONTENTS

Chapter I
The Assistant's Duties: An Overview

Chapter II
Professional and Personal Responsibilities

Chapter III
Materials, Supplies, and Equipment

Chapter IV

Plants and Animals

Chapter V
Biological Cultures

Chapter VI
Formulas and Solutions

Chapter VII
Practical Summaries and Tables

Chapter I
The Assistant's Duties: An Overview

PURPOSES

1. To orient the assistant to his general responsibilities in the department and in the laboratory,
2. To designate special needs within the department and laboratory which require the services of the assistant,
3. To provide general suggestions and procedures for achieving departmental and laboratory improvements,
4. To suggest desirable professional attributes for mastery by the assistant.

BEGINNING THE WORK OF THE ASSISTANT

The departmental assistant is considered an integral part of the teaching staff of the department. As such, he is subject to certain authority, rules, and ethics. Institutional and departmental policies and practices will usually be outlined for new employees at the first departmental staff meeting. In most colleges there is an atmosphere of democratic participation in establishing new and better policies and practices as assistants and staff members work together. The department head is the primary administrator. He also guides orientation to the laboratories. Laboratories are usually directed by members of the permanent teaching staff whose responsibilities are delegated by the department head.

The effective and valuable assistant works closely and receptively at all times with his superiors. He is willing to do menial tasks as well as those that may be noted by the supervising professors. The assistant received his appointment because he is assumed to be intelligent, honest, industrious, and in possession of leadership ability. He must express self-confidence and personal initiative by accepting responsibility and by making decisions, so that he does not continually approach members of the permanent teaching staff with unnecessary questions.

One of the assistant's most desirable traits is punctuality; he should be on time not only for his regular laboratory meetings, but for each staff meeting, conference, and grading session. In some cases, the assistant may be required and should be willing to report to school at least a week prior to the opening of an academic session, in order to meet with the staff and to prepare the laboratories and supply rooms. This entails such activities as becoming generally oriented, checking supplies, and cleaning and arranging equipment.

The assistant must learn to organize his work and budget his time properly; otherwise, he will probably find himself inefficient both on the job and in his scholarship. The assistant will always be working within limits. His class schedule and his work schedule must fall within these recognized limitations.

In departments that employ more than one assistant, it is imperative that good relations prevail between the assistants. A spirit of cooperation must be maintained; this will be made possible by a faithful sharing of departmental responsibilities. Situations may develop in which one or more of the assistants are conducting research activities. The assistant involved with such demands on his time will usually be given fewer responsibilities for the quarter or semester. The assistants, working with other staff members, can generally work out a rotation of major responsibilities so that no particular assistant will be burdened with unfair work loads.

Assistants are required to attend those department staff meetings which the head of the department designates. There will generally be a weekly meeting, at which time the scheduled laboratories and various departmental problems are discussed. If the assistant has anything pertinent to add to these discussions, he should let himself be heard. On occasion the assistant may gain much simply by listening to the presentation by the department head or other permanent staff member.

The assistant has a primary responsibility to become familiar with the general equipment and facilities in the laboratories in which he will be working. He should be sure before the first laboratory period that the laboratory is in order and that all equipment is clean, in working condition, and in its assigned place. All display cases in the laboratory should be checked for cleanliness and correctness of arrangements. As the assistant observes needed changes from time to time, he should consult the department head or other teaching personnel for consent to proceed in making such changes.

The assistant's relationship to students is a teacher-student professional one. Some practices to be avoided include divulging information about grades, becoming too familiar with students, discussing professors in derogatory ways, and, of course, revealing questions to be asked on scheduled tests. While a generally friendly attitude is desirable, the assistant's primary responsibility is to help the student to master subject matter and techniques in the laboratory. He should be available during the entire laboratory period to give help impartially, and only where it is needed.

The assistant should admit that he does not know the answers to some of the questions he will be asked, but he should cooperate with the students in finding the answers through reference and laboratory approaches. He will not lose status by admitting that he does not know all the answers.

Some students like to have the assistant or a professor hovering near most of the time. This is the type of student who will, for example, open a specimen and say, "Now show me what I am supposed to see." Such a student should be made to understand that he must use his laboratory manual and work as independently as possible. In a laboratory that is properly prepared, there are sufficient equipment and good laboratory manuals, and specific directions are given at the beginning of the period. Under these conditions, students are expected to work independently and confidently.

The assistant should avoid giving too much help. He should maintain a teacher-student relationship at all times during laboratory periods, insisting firmly that the laboratory period be a disciplined, organized, and relevant learning experience.

A fundamental duty of the assistant is to present a neat and professional appearance. He should dress in a white laboratory coat.

This may be furnished by the individual or by the department. Laundry services may be furnished by the department; in some cases, the assistant is responsible for laundering his own coats. The assistant needs at least three coats in order to remain neatly attired at all times.

GENERAL INFORMATION FOR THE NEW ASSISTANT

The assistant will find the following information beneficial as he orients himself to his departmental and laboratory responsibilities:

(1) How to use movie and slide projectors,
(2) Where micro-slides are kept and their order of arrangement,
(3) Where specimens are kept and their organization in cabinets and classrooms,
(4) Knowledge of the types and quantities of materials kept in closets, tables, desk drawers, and under sinks,
(5) How to find specific chemicals for various types of laboratory experiments,
(6) Where to find lantern slides and wall charts,
(7) Sources of distilled water,
(8) How to prepare formalin solutions for preserving specimens of various types,
(9) Use and care of such instruments as the autoclave,
(10) Care and handling of live cultures such as Hydra and Amoeba,
(11) Correct replacement of microscopes in cabinets after use,
(12) Care of the aquarium in a general biology laboratory,
(13) Where to find models, such as that of the human.

GENERAL DEPARTMENTAL DUTIES

The assistant should:

(1) Keep stockrooms checked regularly.
(2) Prepare requisition slips for needed supplies.
(3) Check attendance in laboratory and in lecture halls.
(4) Provide typing and general stenographic work in a department that is experiencing a shortage of secretarial help.
(5) Keep a comprehensive class roll and grade book for the laboratory sections in which he is assisting. The record book should include notes on student interests and abilities, with pertinent comments regarding each student.

(6) Keep library books in order and check out books to students. In departments without the services of a librarian this responsibility can become a laborious chore with many records to be kept. Responsibilities should be regularly shared by all the assistants in the department.

(7) Assist with the grading of papers. The assistants are required to aid the professor with grading, tabulating, and recording grades. This responsibility is especially important at the end of the quarter or semester.

(8) Collect and keep records of fees for breakage and equipment replacement.

(9) Prepare bulletin boards. These are a desirable physical feature for each laboratory. A larger centrally located departmental bulletin board is also a great asset. Bulletin boards usually contain departmental news, current articles, book jackets, and information from other colleges and universities concerning the availability of fellowships, assistantships, and departmental offerings in various fields. The assistant should take an active interest in keeping bulletin boards interesting and current. He should work closely with the permanent departmental staff for the procurement of board materials.

(10) Check orders of materials and supplies as these are received. He must make sure that such items are in proper condition. He should separate specimens into different containers when necessary.

(11) Attend the professor's lectures whenever possible.

(12) Read the professional journals to keep abreast of professional developments and to supply new information to students.

(13) Help to plan the social functions of the department and participate in these functions.

(14) Know the location of the custodian's closet for such items as brooms and paper towels.

(15) Confer with the custodian and determine the best time for cleaning blackboards and laboratory floors and windows.

(16) Keep the laboratories neat and orderly.

(17) Report equipment which needs adjustment or repair. The assistant should draw attention to the need for such routine adjustment or repair as it arises.

(18) Handle the occasional problem of student noise, which can reach the point of distracting the attention of others and become a

general nuisance. This type of problem can usually be handled by firm reminders from the assistant. In rare cases, the professor in charge must be consulted.

(19) Prepare comprehensive lesson plans for each laboratory session. Advance planning must be considered one of the most significant duties of the assistant. He should make laboratory preparation file cards for easier preparation of each laboratory. (The nature of such file cards is described in Chapter II.)

GENERAL LABORATORY DUTIES

Ways in which the assistant can give valuable aid in the laboratory include:

(1) Being sure students have a clear concept of the purposes of each laboratory period,

(2) Giving organized and detailed instructions for achieving each laboratory requirement most effectively,

(3) Reviewing subject matter and techniques before each laboratory period so that the assistant is sure he can provide intelligent and specific guidance during the particular period,

(4) Being aware of new methods and techniques that are relevant to the particular situation,

(5) Setting up the various items (such as slides, plastic mounts, preserved and living specimens) and checking the technical and optical quality of demonstrations for each laboratory period,

(6) Demonstrating various techniques, such as dissection of the frog brain or opening the clam, which are difficult for beginners. In such demonstrations, the assistant should keep the groups of students small enough to assure that all students obtain a clear view of the process;

(7) Giving constructive criticism while circulating through the laboratory, observing students' techniques, evaluating their abilities to follow the directions, and noting their general interest. In many cases, the assistant can discover students who are experiencing difficulties in the course, give them help and encouragement, and, if necessary, refer them to the professor;

(8) Recommending the most suitable types of dissecting equipment if students are required to buy their own equipment. The assistant must also be sure that students learn to use properly the dissecting equipment appropriate for each exercise;

(9) Regularly encouraging students to use more than the course textbook by recommending a variety of books, pamphlets, reprints, manuals, and journals pertinent to the course,

(10) Observing and encouraging the special interests and aptitudes of students and referring them to the department head as possible departmental majors and career biologists.

DEPARTMENTAL AND LABORATORY PROBLEMS

Some of the fairly common difficulties experienced by assistants are:

(1) Lack of organization and coordination of personnel and facilities within the department. Under such circumstances, it is difficult for the assistant to recognize his personal, clear-cut responsibilities. This may result in one or two of the assistants doing most of the work. As an effective means of avoiding this problem, the department head may appoint a head assistant with authority to delegate responsibility.

(2) The general types of laboratory problems include (A) spoilage, (B) contamination, (C) death of specimens, and (D) escape of animals from cages. The assistant must be sure that these problems do not arise because of his negligence.

(3) Failure to conduct a weekly check of supplies and equipment, resulting in critical shortages.

(4) Some students attempting to perform dishonestly. The department head will make known to the assistant the policies of the department regarding this problem. If no policies have been established, the assistant should encourage the development of practical guidelines for dealing with dishonesty.

(5) The accumulation of excessive absences by students. The assistant should ask about the policy for handling such absences if it has not been made clear.

(6) The problem of arranging for "make-up" laboratories. The assistants may alternate in supervising such extra sessions. No one will usually be permitted make-up without legitimately excused absences.

PROFESSIONAL ATTRIBUTES

1. The assistant should develop tact. He should make general instruction a cooperative enterprise, using "we" rather than "you."

2. He should develop tolerance. Truth is many-sided. Students should be shown as far as feasible the deeper meaning of their own discoveries of truth and their relation to the discoveries of the professional biologist.

3. He should develop serenity and avoid fretting about such problems as laboratory preparation and the negative results of various exercises. He should profit from all past experiences that have not produced positive outcomes. He should make necessary adjustments when any occasion demands.

4. The assistant must avoid fault-finding and sarcasm, but there are times when a sharp word may be necessary and appropriate. Strict attention must be maintained, with no playful conversation between students when classroom and laboratory work demands such attention.

5. The assistant should be self-reliant, asking questions or referring matters to his superior only when necessary.

6. He should be natural, avoiding mannerisms and affectations.

7. He should strive at all times to give assistance impartially and to treat all students with respect. He must remember that familiarity may breed contempt. The student should be led to realize that the assistant is always ready to provide help on essential matters, but he has no time for campus gossip or pointless discussion.

8. The assistant should support the Socratic method. The laboratory experience should be a vigorous intellectual discovery of knowledge by presenting confidently many questions and problems, searching for the answers, and finding satisfaction to natural curiosity in an atmosphere of free inquiry.

9. He should review the subject matter, biological techniques, and scientific methods again and again. He must not grow weary of approaching the same subject matter from varying angles. Repetition of subject matter, methods, and techniques is a fundamental law of learning in the mastery of biological sciences.

Chapter II
Professional and Personal Responsibilities

PURPOSES

1. To suggest for the assistant a series of methods for professionally aiding the student in the biology program of studies,

2. To outline specific steps for assisting biology students toward solution of a variety of problems encountered during course experiences,

3. To provide references and suggestions for securing and utilizing various resources as means of adding to the effectiveness of departmental offerings,

4. To provide guidelines for procuring materials, supplies, and equipment and for utilizing the assistance of professional facilities and personnel outside the department,

5. To stimulate the assistant toward continued study and growth in proficiency as a member of the biology profession,

6. To provide specific suggestions for application by the assistant in seeking technical and teaching proficiency as a member of the biology department.

THE ASSISTANT, THE STUDENT, AND THE SCIENTIFIC METHOD

The assistant should emphasize by precept and example for the student that the process in any scientific investigation is fundamentally simple. Initially a question is asked. The stimulus to ask the question may originate from an observation made in a previous investigation, from an article read in a technical journal, or from an experience outside the laboratory. Forming this question is the crucial initial aspect of the experiment. Great discoveries are made by men who formulate clear and simple questions. Without the intelligent question, the scientist literally does not know that he is seeking a logical answer.

9

Once the question has been asked, the investigator proceeds to plan the design of his investigation. He selects an appropriate animal or the most satisfactory chemical, physical, and biological procedures to compile data from which will come an answer to his question as he performs his investigation under controlled conditions. He attempts, wherever possible, to make quantitative measurements rather than to satisfy personal "value" estimations or judgments.

Of prime importance in the planning stage is the choice of his controls. He needs quantitative information on all variables that might influence the outcome of the experiment either positively or negatively. Considerable experience is required in order to control a study properly. Among the sources of variation which must be considered are sex, age, weight, genetic background, nutritional condition, season of the year, temperature, humidity, lighting, time of day, and method of housing. All or any of these may be improperly interpreted in terms of cause and effect. These and other variables can usually be controlled by selecting two animals or groups of animals, two plants or groups of plants, or two situations that are as identical as possible. One serves as the "control," the other as the "experimental." For example, the question is asked, "What effect does removal of the adrenal glands have on blood sodium concentration?" Two animals undergo an operation, but the adrenal glands are removed from only one. The other animal is "sham-operated" and is subjected to every other aspect of the investigation except that part which is contained in the investigator's question. The sham-operated animal is the control. By comparing the changes in blood sodium of the control with the changes in the experimental animal, one may conclude that adrenalectomy causes a reduction of the concentration of this blood constituent.

Once decisions have been made about the design of the experiment, the scientist conducts the investigation and carefully documents all his observations with faithful objectivity.

He does not allow personal prejudices or preconceived (a priori) ideas to influence his thinking and observations. Furthermore, when the investigation has been completed, he prepares a report of his work so that the observations themselves, not a priori notions, guide him to a logical, rational conclusion. If the question originally asked was a good one, and if the design was appropriate, the proper conclusions should follow by application of deductive logic.

Continuous use of the scientific method should characterize every aspect of the student's procedures in the various biology courses. This method is as fundamental as the proper method of using the microscope in a daily laboratory. The assistant must constantly emphasize its importance and illustrate its application as he guides the student through various exercises.

THE ASSISTANT, THE STUDENT, AND THE LABORATORY

The assistant should emphasize to the student the general purposes of the laboratory experiences: (1) to enable the student to see and examine specimens and materials such as charts, models, and slides that he cannot deal with satisfactorily in large groups or classes; (2) to stimulate the student to ask questions and to explore further the topics presented in textbook assignments and class lectures; (3) to enable the student to observe and to understand some of the functionings of various biological systems; (4) to help the student to achieve insight into the scientific method and how it functions; (5) to develop and broaden student interests and curiosity; and (6) to teach the importance of accuracy and neatness in experimental work.

Laboratory exercises will usually be done in two- or three-hour periods each week. The assistant should see that students enter quietly and go at once to their assigned seats to await instructions. Each student should be held responsible for the appearance of his table and locker space. The assistant should check the condition of all equipment at the beginning of the period, and anything out of order should be recorded for correction as soon as possible. Cleanliness and orderliness are of utmost importance in all laboratory procedures. The assistant should hold the student accountable for the condition of his reagent bottles, glassware, dissecting pans, microscope, microscope slides, and other equipment, and these must always be in good condition at the end of each session. Laboratory stools should be left under tables. Scrap paper, towels, and other waste materials should be put into containers supplied by the assistant. The tables must be left clean and dry.

The assistant should help the professor to provide demonstrations of specimens or views for individual observation. Such demonstrations are designed to acquaint the student with a wider range of material than would be possible through the routine group laboratory procedure. The student should be aided in his careful examination of all such demonstrations, and he should be given sufficient time for making any necessary notations or sketches.

The assistant cannot overemphasize the significance of the student's attitude toward his laboratory work. Tardiness, unnecessary noise, frequent and prolonged absences from the laboratory, dependence upon neighbors, and other similar practices are obviously inconsistent with best work. The assistant should encourage an attentive, independent, responsible, and conscientious attitude in the laboratory. He should emphasize that these qualities in the student are certain to result in an improvement in the work achieved. If the assistant shows that he takes his work seriously and that it deserves such consideration, then the student is much more likely to develop these qualities.

The assistant should supply the student with the appropriate materials and specimens, which are the foundation of the work, in good condition. He should emphasize the importance of the instructions given in the laboratory manual or in prepared worksheets. The student should carefully study each specimen and secure all possible information concerning it, observing details as well as general relationships. The assistant should encourage the student to search for things that the manual does not describe or that vary from the given descriptions.

At the end of each laboratory period the assistant should require each student to place all specimens, equipment, slides, and microscopes in their proper places. All apparatus should be secured and permanent slides accounted for. The table should be cleared so that students of the following sections will have a clean place to work. The assistant should receive drawings and reports at the end of each period. The student's name and section number should be placed on each page; the pages should be clipped together.

When examining fresh or preserved anatomical specimens, the assistant should justify their use as materials from which the student can learn, at first hand, facts about which he read or heard. The student should not think of them as parts of some person's or animal's body but as appropriate means to satisfy intellectual curiosity. He should suppress attitudes of morbid curiosity. As the scientific method of approach to dissection and demonstrations is cultivated, the student need never be distressed by the specimens and processes which he may be called upon to handle or witness.

Laboratory offerings should be set up to keep the average student occupied for the entire laboratory period, allowing for periodic breaks for moments of relaxation or refreshment. If a student finishes his work before a period is over the assistant should check to make sure that he has not hurried carelessly through the exercise. Generally, each experiment must be completed before the next laboratory period.

The assistant should keep in mind a variety of extra experiments or exercises. He may encourage such activities by students with special interest or ability or who are interested in becoming departmental majors or career biologists.

Some departments will require term papers, reports, or term projects and exhibits. These will be assigned and completed at times to be stipulated by the professor. (The assistant will find special information regarding such requirements in a later section of this chapter.)

The assistant should encourage the student to read laboratory directions carefully and understandingly before beginning his work. The student should not rely on what his neighbor tells him; the neighbor may be wrong. The student should know what he intends to do and why as he pursues a laboratory activity. If he is not sure he should always feel free to ask the assistant.

The assistant should require the student to budget his time properly. Excessive time spent on any one phase of the laboratory offering will naturally prevent the student from completing the total requirements of the scheduled laboratory period.

The assistant may wish to prepare supplementary laboratory outlines to be used as guides and suggestions. The laboratory director or the department head may wish to work with the assistant in the preparation of such guides. Outlines so prepared may contain more materiol than can be covered in one laboratory period, but they should not be intended as guides for "regular laboratory" exercises in which the student is expected to do individual dissections and to make personal observations. They should be used to clarify directions, to outline more specifically a period's offering, and to provide suggested follow-up group activities and discussions.

The assistant should encourage students to list in their notebooks the facts they have learned and also the questions that have been raised but not answered. The questions should be submitted to the assistant for discussion in future lectures by the professor or for discussion during laboratory sessions.

The assistant must routinely require each student to keep careful notes and to make accurate drawings. Each student should collect the data from experiments in the form of tables, graphs, or concise statements. Questions at the conclusion of the manual experiment sections should be answered by the student completely and thoughtfully.

The assistant should always strive to develop student understanding of the physiological significance of the observed results as well as the conclusions that can be safely derived from the data. In order to explain the data gathered, the student should be encouraged to read pertinent material in assigned tests or available reference books and to discuss his observations with the assistant.

Each student must have opportunity for learning to use the microscope correctly. Time spent in mastering this procedure will pay dividends throughout the biology experience.

The assistant should emphasize that the biological sciences require special techniques and skills comparable to those of the surgeon and that there is a right and a wrong way to conduct these various procedures. The right way brings success; the wrong way brings frustration, poor results, and loss of valuable time. Perfection in laboratory techniques will require patient, mature attention and the application of a professional attitude on the part of assistant and sudent. It is desirable that the student learn to treat each laboratory assignment as if he were being specifically graded on all of his performances during that period.

The assistant should always wear his laboratory coat, and provision should be made for appropriate dress for the student. Laboratory clothing will protect the personal clothing normally worn and lends a desirable professional appearance to the departmental activity program.

Students should not be permitted to eat in the laboratory. Hands should, as a matter of course, be kept away from the mouth. Laboratory labels should be moistened with tap water instead of the tongue.

Accidents of any type should be reported promptly to the assistant. Such accidents as burning or cutting the flesh, spilling infectious material, or breaking test tubes or Petri dishes may occur. The assistant should be sure that a first-aid kit is available for immediate use, and he should be familiar with general first-aid principles.

Tables and work areas should be kept clear of such items as coats and purses. Laboratory space should be used only for laboratory equipment and notebooks. The assistant must make sure that racks are available for clothing.

Students must avoid accumulating unclean glassware, papers, and personal belongings in their laboratory desks or lockers. Each student should be responsible for cleaning his own equipment and properly replacing it for later use.

BIOLOGY LECTURES

Biology lectures presented by a teaching member of the staff will deal with fundamental biological principles, leaving morphological details largely as a part of the laboratory work of the assistant. The assistant must remember that the class lectures may not be designed primarily as specific preparation for the laboratory work. Whenever possible, the professor will correlate lectures with laboratory work, but for practical reasons a close correlation is not always possible, or even desirable. In the time available, the classroom lecturer can hope only to present the barest outline of the course. The assistant can effectively supplement the lecture material by keeping in touch with the content of the lectures and by planning laboratory offerings of relevant topics as near as possible to the time such topics are presented in the lecture periods.

GENERAL NOTE TAKING

Apart from notes on specific experiments, the assistant should require general student note taking in the laboratory, including items developed independently from the student's laboratory observations and information received formally and informally from the assistant or professor. Notes should be kept ready for inspection by the assistant at any time.

The assistant should encourage the students to consolidate all the quarter's or semester's laboratory observations and conclusions in a logical notebook sequence. The student should arrange his notebook according to the order in which he did the laboratory experiments. At the beginning of the quarter or semester, the assistant should outline for the students an orderly way of keeping the records of all their experiments. Not only can the notebook become a tangible record of what the student has accomplished, but it can reveal to the assistant a number of strengths and weaknesses of the method of student work.

THE DEMONSTRATION METHOD

The demonstration method of teaching is invaluable, as, by objectification, it makes certain parts of the subject matter clear which could otherwise not be fully understood. The assistant can use the method in ways to realize a number of further advantages:

(1) It is one of the least expensive methods of achieving laboratory learnings.

(2) It is time-saving.

(3) All students can see the same operation and technique at the same time.

The assistant should prepare to explain each item of a specimen, instrument, or process being demonstrated, thus ensuring that each student sees and interprets all the work in the same manner.

The demonstration approach, when combined with well-directed discussions and actual laboratory experiences, will prove extremely rewarding.

THE LABORATORY METHOD

"Laboratory method" is an expression that is not easily definable. In most cases, it means that each student or pair of students is provided with specimens, a work guide, and essential equipment for making dissections or studying biological materials by classification or otherwise. There are distinct advantages inherent in the laboratory method, even when it is applied to single periods and in rooms not designed primarily as laboratories. The methods and provisions of the laboratory can be considered fundamentally useful tools of science.

The assistant should keep in mind the specific types of advantages provided for his students through their laboratory opportunities:

(1) The laboratory means learning by doing.

(2) The student has opportunity for handling materials.

(3) The student learns to follow directions carefully.

(4) He performs experiments, records observations and results, summarizes data, and draws conclusions.

(5) He learns to handle apparatus, and he has opportunity to do much thinking for himself.

Basic skills and techniques developed in the laboratory will have distinct value in other courses and in professional work into which the student may enter later.

The assistant should constantly emphasize that the first requisite in the laboratory is keen, meticulous, and patient observation of facts that are accurately and faithfully recorded. The student must learn to report only what he actually sees, even though it may not agree with written descriptions and pictures The assistant must help the student to see that the specimen is always right. The assistant should take pride in imbuing students with the spirit of the scientific method, encouraging them to make full use of the opportunity for training in its use. Between assistant and student the laboratory method involves observation, experimentation, analysis, and conclusions. The conclusions reached by the student and accepted by the assistant must always square with the facts. Science does not recognize mere rumor or guesswork. Objective, factual evidence will be discovered for supplanting the mere word of authority, if assistant and student maintain the true scientific attitude.

THE LABORATORY MANUAL

The assistant should help the student to understand that the laboratory manual is not to be regarded as a handbook of formulas and directions that are to be blindly followed. It is designed merely as an aid to the student; it will be supplemented at all times by the interpretive aid provided by the assistant. The laboratory manual will serve very effectively to point out various structures to be observed; it will formulate certain problems and suggest methods for solving them; it will suggest various drawings that will be helpful in recording facts; it will propose questions that may lead to correct conclusions derived from the facts observed or data obtained through personal experimentation. The thoughtful student will soon come to rely on the combination of assistant and laboratory manual as he sees many more structures and as he frames many more problems than those which can be suggested in the textbook or manual alone.

PREPARING DEMONSTRATIONS

When setting up demonstrations, the assistant should be sure to use the proper type of magnifier. The appropriate one is determined by such factors as the amount of magnification needed and light conditions. Higher magnification than is necessary should never be used. A stereoscopic microscope is valuable for studying glomerular function, circulation in the lung, or functioning villi, since it shows depth, for instance. Hand and desk viewers with Kodachrome slides may be used to supplement the use of microscope slides and microscopes.

MODELS, CHARTS, DIAGRAMS, PICTURES, AND BLACKBOARDS

These may serve as aids in objectifying written or spoken words by substituting for specimens. The professor or assistant may also have students construct them as aids to student understanding. The way they are used in the laboratory is generally decided by the assistant. The production of such study aids need not be undertaken by all students, but some students will demonstrate a great interest in such activities.

Good printed charts should be obtained from various biological supply houses, as well as diagrams from a variety of texts. The assistant must be careful that the complexity and detail of various pictorializations do not prove a source of confusion, however. A much more crude diagrammatic illustration built up by the assistant with chalk on the blackboard, adding each part with the development of each idea, will often be much better as a teaching aid than some of the more expensive completed charts. The assistant may well use the blackboard drawing plus the chart as an effective combination. The assistant should not hesitate to use the blackboard because of a lack of artistic ability; blackboard drawings should be purely diagrammatic, not artistic.

The assistant should recognize that the department's selection of purchased models or wall charts must be made with considerable care as to their accuracy for the various courses in which they will be used. It is possible to invest much money in materials that are of little use.

Models have the advantage of depicting objects in three dimensions, though they usually lack detail and may at times furnish distorted and unnatural concepts. For example, a starfish could be modeled and painted so as to give students a fairly accurate idea of the animal in the laboratory, but a clay or plaster model of a jellyfish is a poor representation to the student who has never seen one at the seashore.

Students may sometimes make their own models from water-softened modeling clay. These, when well done, may be painted, mounted, and kept by the student, after receiving course credit, or they may be claimed by the department. With the cooperation of the fine arts and manual arts classes, the biology department can achieve good integrated projects produced by students.

The assistant should also not overlook the possibilities of amateur photography as an aid for the total biology experience. The assistant who is interested in photography may accumulate an interesting and valuable library of pictures; he may also encourage the formation of a departmental collection or a biological sciences photography club. Such an organization has very special application to field study, where unusual views or ecological situations may be obtained.

SLIDES, FILMSTRIPS, AND PHOTOMICROGRAPHS

Slides, filmstrips, and especially photomicrographs are valuable accessories to the teaching assistant. Photomicrographs are a means of making the still projector do the work of a larger number of microscopes when the department does not possess sufficient microscopes. Good photographs of microscopic preparations can be enlarged without loss of essential detail. When these are projected upon the screen, each student sees what he would view if he were provided with a microscope and microscope slide. Such projection technique has the additional advantage that all students see the same thing at the same time. The photographs are usually made from uniformly good preparations, but while this technique will show large or gross structure, such as pollen grains or the veins of insect wings, it is useless for details of cell structure or microorganisms because the detail is lost when the image is enlarged for room visibility. The technique may be used for a very small group, however, and it is excellent for making enlarged drawings directly from microscope slides.

QUIZZING

The general purpose of quizzing is to bring together and correlate the theoretical aspects and general principles of the lectures with the practical work of the laboratory. Oral and written quizzes should be held at intervals, but much of the work time should be devoted to student discussion. Various professors follow different quizzing practices, but the student is generally responsible for lecture material, reading assignments, and laboratory work. The assistant should bring special attention to the questions included in the laboratory manual and relate these to questions found in the textbooks as well as to the lecture notes given during class and laboratory time.

LABORATORY QUIZZES

The student should be held responsible for answering the assistant's questions regarding the information in the laboratory manual as well as additional information provided by the assistant. The assistant should also feel free to ask the student to point out structures in specimens to which attention has been directed. The student will find it helpful to study carefully the assignment for the day before he comes to the laboratory.

THE PRACTICAL EXAMINATION

Laboratory practical examinations should be held at intervals during the course. The assistant will generally have complete charge of setting up the practical examination, under supervision of the lecturer in charge of the course. At such times, the student will be examined upon the actual material studied in the laboratory, including demonstrations and individual work. He should be able to identify the various specimens and structures called for and in general be prepared to answer questions based on work done in the laboratory. (The practical examination is treated in detail in a subsequent section of this chapter).

ANSWERING STUDENT QUESTIONS

When a student presents a question to the assistant, every effort should be made by the assistant to answer it himself, either from specimens or from his own knowledge; or the assistant may find it necessary to search for the answer by consulting various references or securing the help of the lecturing professor or instructor. The assistant should follow this logical order in dealing with questions, always trying to answer as many of the questions himself as possible.

Time should be given during regular staff meetings to a consideration of the troublesome laboratory topics, and effort should be made to decide upon correct answers in anticipation of student questions. The assistant should never try to appear knowledgeable regarding any question unless he is sure of himself. His attitude may well be, "I don't know the answer to that, but we'll find out together."

ANALYZING AND RATING STUDENT PROGRESS

The assistant should at all times be cognizant of the progress the student is making. The assistant is also in an excellent position to help the student to analyze his difficulties. He can become familiar with a student's problems by careful observation of the laboratory work, by checking drawings and laboratory quizzes, by conferences with the student, and by conferences with the professor regarding the student.

It may be helpful to inform the student whether he is high, low, or average in relation to other students of the class or laboratory. Checking himself against the other members of his class will help him to appreciate his own standing. Such repeated checking will indicate his progress. His standing at the close of the quarter or semester should be a fair measure of his achievement under the guidance of the assistant and the lecturing professor or instructor.

TEACHING THE USE OF THE MICROSCOPE

The assistant should regularly emphasize the proper methods to use and care for the microscope. Skill in the use of this instrument is fundamentally important in the biological sciences, and proficiency calls for practice and review of basic steps. The student is held responsible for the instrument's condition. He should be encouraged to report at once to the assistant any imperfection or damage.

The assistant should demonstrate the proper method of carrying the microscope by holding the pillar with one hand while supporting the base with the other. It should be emphasized that microscopes must be put away with the low-power objective in place and the diaphragm open.

To avoid eyestrain in using the microscope, it is important that the student be relaxed. He should sit squarely in front of the microscope at such a height that he can look directly into the ocular and down through the tube without strain. While doing this, he should always keep both eyes open. He will find such open-eye use of the instrument much less tiring. This ability will develop with practice.

In order to identify the dominant eye, the assistant should have the student tear a one-inch hole in the center of a sheet of paper. Holding this sheet with one hand at arm's length, he should look through the hole at some small object across the room with first the left eye and then the right. If the object sighted remains in the hole, the student is left-eyed; if the hole appears to move, the student is either right-eyed or he has no eye dominance. The dominance of the right eye can be determined in the same manner as the left.

It is not necessary to wear glasses in miscroscopic work if the person is only nearsighted or farsighted. The microscope can be focused for these defects. In the case of astigmatism, however, the glasses must be worn, since the microscope cannot correct this condition.

Using the Compound Microscope

Two methods can be used to examine an object under the microscope. In the first method, the object is examined by reflected light. This method is ordinarily employed when viewing objects with the naked eye. The object under the microscope must be illuminated from above so that light falling on its surface is reflected through the lenses of the microscope into the eye. In the second method, the object is viewed by transmitted light. In this case, the illumination must be beneath the object and come through it to the lenses of the microscope and the eye. In order to get sufficient light to pass through the object, the mirror under the stage of the microscope is adjusted to reflect a beam of light from a bright source, such as a window or a lamp, through the opening of the iris diaphragm and up through the tube of the microscope.

When viewed by transmitted light, the interior of an object becomes visible because the materials of which it is composed differ in their capacity for transmitting light. An object to be observed by transmitted light must be thin enough to be transparent. It is usually immersed in a liquid or solid transparent substance, such as Canada balsam, and covered with a cover glass. In this way, reflections from the surface of the object, which confuse the image formed by the transmitted light, are largely avoided, making it possible for the student to view the internal structure clearly.

Examination of a Prepared Slide with Low Power

The student should practice techniques with a microscope slide on which a small piece of paper with a printed word has been mounted in water or Canada balsam and covered with a cover glass. He should place the slide on the stage of the microscope with the cover glass up and the word in the correct position to be read with the naked eye. If the low-power objective is not already in line with the tube of the microscope, the nosepiece should be turned so as to bring it into line with the tube. Since the object will be observed by transmitted light, the mirror must be adjusted so that light from a window or a lamp passes up through the slide and into the objective. When the mirror is properly adjusted, the part of the slide over the iris diaphragm will appear bright as the student looks at it with the naked eye. The student should not yet attempt to look through the microscope, but he should bend down toward the table and put one eye on a level with the stage of the microscope so that he can see clearly the distance between the bottom of the objective and the microscope slide. Then, using the coarse adjustment, he should carefully lower the tube until the bottom of the low-power objective is about ⅛ inch from the top of the slide. Then, and not until then, he should look through the ocular and, while doing so, gradually raise the tube by means of the coarse adjustment and move the slide about on the stage until the object comes into his view and he sees it in sharp focus. He may find that further adjustment of the mirror is necessary in order to get the best illumination. He can practice centering the light by swinging the low-power objective into place and lowering the body tube until the end of the objective is about one centimeter from the upper surface of the substage condenser. The mirror should then be moved about until uniform illumination is provided for the microscope field.

The student must practice controlling the light with the iris diaphragm. The assistant should emphasize that the student routinely focuses *upward* when looking into the ocular to observe any slide preparation on the stage.

Distance from Object to Objective

Using a ruler, the student should measure exactly the distance from the bottom of the objective to the top of the cover glass above a specimen being observed in focus. He should note this distance carefully for future reference. In future work, this distance will generally bring the specimen into focus, ready for study.

Orientation of Objects

While looking through the ocular, the student should move the microscope slide about on the stage until he finds some of the letters of the word. He should then compare the orientation of one of the letters as seen under the microscope with its orientation as seen with the naked eye. He should also compare the direction in which the letter seems to move when seen through the microscope with the direction in which it is actually moved by his hand.

Determining Magnification

The magnification of the microscope may be found by comparing the actual size of the object as seen with the naked eye at a distance of 10 inches with the size of the object as seen through the microscope when the image is projected to a distance of 10 inches from the eye. With a little practice, it is possible to look through the instrument with one eye while the other eye is directed at a piece of white paper on the table at the base of the microscope. More accurate measurements can be obtained with a camera lucida instrument.

By multiplying the magnifying power of the ocular (generally stamped on the metal cylinder of the ocular lens as "10x") by the x power stamped on the objectives (generally 10, 44, and 97), the student can determine how much the specimen has been magnified.

Drawing an Object Seen with the Microscope

The student should attempt to draw the alphabet letter at approximately the same magnification as oriented and seen under the microscope. For comparison he should, on the same sheet, draw the letter "natural size" and in its actual orientation.

Examination of a Prepared Slide with High Power

The objectives of a microscope are usually mounted on the nosepiece so as to be parfocal. If this is the case, in order to bring an object already in focus under the low power into focus under the high power, it is only necessary to turn the nosepiece so that the high-power objective is in line with the tube (of course, the height of the tube must not be disturbed in the process). The student should turn the nosepiece to bring the higher power into position without touching the cover glass with the lower end of the objective. If the objectives are parfocal, the object will be approximately in focus and may be brought into sharpest focus by slightly manipulating the fine adjustment. In this case, a small portion of the printed letter will appear as a mass of black or white fibers.

If the objectives are not mounted on the microscope so as to be parfocal, it will be necessary, in order to bring the high power into focus, to pursue a method somewhat similar to that used in bringing the low power into focus. With the high power in position and with one eye on a level with the stage of the microscope, the student lowers the tube of the microscope until the lower end of the objective nearly touches the cover glass. Then while looking through the ocular, he gradually raises the tube with the fine adjustment until the object comes into focus. If his first attempt to bring the object into focus fails, he must not focus downward, since this will probably cause the slide to break and may damage the objective. Such failure to achieve sharp focus is probably due to one or more of the following causes: (1) the objective was not sufficiently close to the cover glass before the student began to raise it; (2) the coarse adjustment may have been used instead of the fine adjustment, thereby leading to a too-rapid raising of the tube; or (3) the mirror or the iris diaphragm may not have been adjusted to bring sufficient light to the object, since the light should be brighter when the student plans to turn to a higher-powered objective.

Oil Immersion Technique

Carefully guided by the assistant, the student focuses in on the prepared slide with lower power and centers the part of the material in which he is interested. Without touching any of the adjustment knobs, the high-power objective is turned into place. If necessary, center again the part of the material under observation. When the material has been definitely centered, raise the high-power objective about ½ inch upward from the slide. Add a drop of immersion oil to the cover glass. This drop should be placed so that the oil-immersion lens, when lowered, will touch the surface of the oil. Next, move the oil-immersion objective carefully into place. This objective has a black band as an identifying marker. Lower it until the objective just touches the tip of the oil. Now focus in with the fine adjustment knob.

After the student has mastered this technique, he should wipe off his slide and oil-immersion objective. This is absolutely necessary; some immersion oils will form crusts on the objectives. The regular objectives must not be used for oil-immersion purposes, for if they are, not only will the student not see the object clearly, but the objectives will be smeared. (Microscopes used in introductory work may lack the special oil-immersion objective.)

Angular and Numerical Aperture

The term "angular aperture" is used to denote the angle between the most divergent rays that may pass through the objective to form the image. The angular aperture of an objective is a factor that helps to determine the microscope's resolving power. In addition, the index of refraction of the immersion medium (material between object and objective) must be taken into account. The true measure of the resolving power is the numerical aperture (the higher the numerical aperture value the greater the resolving power), which may be expressed as follows:

$$\text{numerical aperture} = (N) \frac{\text{sine angular aperture}}{2}$$

where N equals the index of refraction of the medium from which the light enters the objective.

Rules to Be Observed by Students

The assistant should post or distribute the following general rules for students using the microscope:

(1) Always focus upward when your eye is situated at the eyepiece. If you focus down, there is danger of injuring the lens system and the specimen.

(2) Always use a cover glass when you examine objects mounted in water or other fluids, or when you use the high-power objectives.

(3) When rotating objectives, always be sure that they do not contact the stage or slide when the higher-powered objective is turned into its position above the specimen. Neglect of this precaution can ruin many good slides and lenses.

(4) Always use the lowest power that will show sufficiently the details you need to see.

(5) Use the high power only to see details that cannot be seen with the low power and only on objects that are covered by a cover glass.

(6) When using the high power, do not focus downward unless you know there is ample space between the bottom of the objective and the upper surface of the cover glass.

(7) Always raise the high-power objective sufficiently upward before removing your slide.

(8) Do not touch the lens with anything except the special lens paper provided by the departmental assistant for that purpose.

(9) To clean an objective or ocular, breathe on the surface of the glass and rub lightly with the lens paper. Use only fresh lens paper and use a sheet only once. If the lens does not yield to this method of cleaning, consult the assistant, who will supply you with xylol or alcohol for moistening your lens paper and carefully stroking the lens.

(10) Never force a part of the microscope to move. If it does not work easily, call the assistant for advice.

(11) Never touch the glass parts of the microscope with your fingers.

(12) Proficiency in use and care of the microscope develops only with practice and repetition.

PREPARATION OF DRAWINGS

Drawings form a major part of the laboratory record. A number of drawings are generally required in all biology courses. The assistant has the responsibility for preparing the student to draw neatly, accurately, and in accordance with certain standards for acceptable biology drawings. (A checklist for use in correcting drawings will be found in a subsequent section of this chapter.)

The student's drawings may be considered comparable to the theme written in an English course or the report for a history class; they require concentration and careful attention to details. They are also a part of the professional training in the preparation of scientific records.

Drawings graded by the assistant must be rated on accuracy and completeness rather than on artistic merit, since the ability to draw varies widely among students.

The assistant can readily recognize text illustrations that have been used as substitutes for original drawings. Such substitutes must be considered dishonest. When the assistant encounters duplicate work that is suspicious, he may call for explanations from both students.

If, to complete a study, it should become desirable to copy a drawing from some text, the assistant should be fully aware of the student's use of the text, and credit should be given to the source.

The production of biological drawings is a form of scientific note taking. Accuracy is the most important essential of a good drawing. In practice, this means that the student should first make a careful, thorough study of the specimen; no drawing should be attempted until this has been done. When such observations have been made, the drawing itself then becomes the method or technique of recording them. The assistant should provide the student with typical structures or specimens, and the student should faithfully record only what he sees. The student must draw the object itself, instead of copying a textbook illustration, blackboard diagram, or a fellow student's drawing.

The drawing requirement helps to assure that the student will see things in detail. Only when the student attempts to draw an object does he really begin to see it comprehensively, and only by drawing an object can he tell whether he has really seen it.

The assistant must make sure that all drawings are made in the laboratory with a hard, sharp pencil. A clear outline is the first essential of a good drawing. When an object shows generally uniform detail over a large area, this detail should be done for only a small portion; it will be understood that the general area is similar.

Drawings should be labeled by ruling fine lines out toward the margin and writing the names of structures on the label lines. The student should not use any system of lettering or numbering. This is confusing and time consuming. A title should accompany each drawing to specify as clearly as possible the object drawn. To this should be added a statement of the magnification.

Drawings should be neatly made, classified according to subject treated, and arranged symmetrically on the page. If the drawing is to be finished in ink, black India ink and a suitable drawing pen (not a fountain pen) should be used for both drawing and labeling.

Rules for Drawing

The assistant can profitably share with students the following list of drawing rules:

(1) Always keep a sharp point on the pencil.
(2) Make sketches only after all questions have been answered regarding the view to be drawn.

(3) Study the object carefully and sketch lightly. Finish the drawing with the drawing pencil, brought to a very fine point with a piece of sandpaper. A soft pencil may be used for blocking in and sketching, but for the finished drawings only a hard pencil (4H or 6H) with a round, sharp point should be used.

(4) For shading effects, only one of the conventional methods, such as stippling or hatching, should be used.

(5) The type of paper upon which drawings are to be made should be designated by the assistant.

(6) Use an eraser of good quality, which will not soil the paper.

(7) A millimeter ruler will be needed for checking proportions and labeling structures. The student should use a ruler even if he prints fairly well.

(8) Arrange separate figures on the sheet in a symmetrical pattern.

(9) Each figure should be large enough to show all details clearly, as well as accurately. It should be mainly an outline (a line drawing), and necessarily somewhat diagrammatic.

(10) Extensive repetition of repeated parts is unnecessary; instead, show a few parts with careful details.

(11) Avoid sketchy lines; be definite. Each line should have a specific purpose.

(12) First mark out lightly the extreme length and width (or diameter) to be occupied by a figure. If the specimen is bilaterally symmetrical, a faint longitudinal axis should be drawn as a temporary guide in the placement of parts. Then the figure should be outlined lightly. Estimate the proportionate size of some component parts in relation to the entire specimen, and these should be marked on the area outlined for the drawing. The major features should be drawn, and lines should be strengthened as necessary. Then comes erasure of the unneeded marks. Space should be left, preferably at the right of the figure, for the labels. The assistant should help students to determine which parts are to be labeled in each figure. There should be no crossing of label lines. Place all labels parallel with the top of the plate, printed against the edge of a ruler. Labels should not be underlined. Use small print.

(13) For parts not seen in a specimen, consult any demonstration material and add the missing parts to the figure; otherwise, note the part as "not seen" on the drawings.

(14) Under each individual drawing give the figure number, title, and

the approximate scale of reduction or enlargement as compared with the specimen, as the following:

The Frog: Circulatory System, Ventral View, 2X

(15) For drawings of microscopic subjects, the lenses and magnification may be noted; for example:

L.P. 5x (low-power objective or 5x ocular)
440x (if magnified 440 times)
¼x (if drawn ¼ actual size)

(16) On each separate drawing sheet, place your name and any other data indicated by the assistant, such as plate number, date, laboratory section, and seat number.

(17) Sometimes it is desirable to enlarge and at other times to reduce the size of the object in the drawing. Whenever this is necessary, the portions should be enlarged or reduced equally in all dimensions.

(18) Darker and lighter areas of the drawing may be indicated by increasing or decreasing the number of stippling or hatching marks per unit area. Objects lying below others may be indicated by broken lines.

(19) At the top of the drawing, print the title of the exercise in large block letters. The lines that connect the labels to the figure should be done with a ruler, but they need not be horizontal.

(20) If any of the drawings are colored, the following scheme should be observed:

ectoderm	light blue
endoderm	light yellow
mesoderm	medium red
nerve cord and nerves	white
brain	white
liver, spleen, and kidneys	brown
pancreas, thymus, thyroid, and fat bodies	yellow
notochord	green
arteries	dark red
bones	gray
gills and lungs	pink
gall bladder	green

(21) The student should correct errors called to his attention in drawings returned to him, and see that these errors are avoided in the future.

Whenever the criticism involves such items as size, proportion, and general form, corrections need not be attempted on the drawing itself, but inaccuracies in the representation of such items as details, labeling, and spelling should be corrected immediately on the drawing. The corrected plates should be placed in proper order and kept by the student until called for by the assistant for final checking and evaluation at the end of the quarter or semester.

Criticisms to Improve Drawing Skills

The following criticism sections contain numbered statements or types of specific criticisms regarding (1) observations by the student; (2) condition of the drawing; (3) over-all appearance of the plate; and (4) the student as a laboratory worker.

The assistant should have copies of these sections duplicated and titled "Drawing Criticisms." Each student should be provided with a personal copy.

The assistant should regularly receive the drawings from students and use these criticisms for calling the student's attention to his drawing errors. The assistant should mark the appropriate criticism number from this list onto the student's drawing and return the drawing. The student may then find the meaning of the numbered criticism conveniently by checking his marked drawing against his personal "Drawing Criticisms" sheet.

The assistant must emphasize to the student that errors in drawings are to be expected. The challenge is to improve constantly in observation and drawing ability so that errors do not continue over a period of time.

Criticisms of Drawing Observations

1. Observe specimens more carefully.
2. Show more contrast in specimen parts.
3. Too little detail
4. Too diagrammatic
5. Did you actually see this?
6. Incorrect proportion of parts
7. Refer to texts or notes.
8. Refer to various laboratory aids more frequently.

9. Too small
10. Too large
11. Too much detail

Criticisms of Condition of Drawing

12. Messy
13. Not clear
14. Spelling
15. Use hard pencil.
16. Erasure
17. Sketchiness
18. Stipple. Do not smudge.
19. Use dotted lines to show missing sections or parts.
20. Neatness
21. Carelessness
22. This must be redrawn.
23. Give only what is asked for.
24. Unnecessary
25. Drawing not dark enough

Criticisms of Over-all Appearance of Plate

26. Crowded
27. Incorrect type of paper
28. Incorrect labeling
29. Print more carefully.
30. Incorrect plate and/or figure number and/or position
31. Underline generic and specific names.
32. Need better arrangement of specimen and/or labeling on plate
33. Upper- and lower-case letters
34. Use ruler.
35. Need better arrangement of specimen and/or labels on plate
36. Incomplete labeling

Criticisms of the Student as a Laboratory Worker

37. A good attitude is always an asset.
38. You can do much better work.
39. You are improving.
40. This was explained in lecture and/or laboratory.
41. See assistant about this.
42. Show more pride in your work.

43. Make better use of laboratory instruments.
44. Improve your dissection techniques.
45. Budget time properly.
46. Plan drawing schedule more carefully.
47. Do more independent work.

DIRECTING DISSECTIONS

The assistant is responsible for preparing students to make informative dissections of specimens. This requires development of good dissection technique. A first essential is that the student be taught the nature and limitations of his dissection instruments.

There are three fundamental dissecting tools: scissors, probe, and forceps. Ideally, the student should have available two pairs of sharp scissors—a small pair for finer work, and a larger one for gross dissections. They should cut without the necessity for pushing and pulling. In general, the scissors will serve adequately for all cutting jobs. A scalpel may not only be unnecessary, but scissors may be safer both for the student and for the specimen. Scissors are much less likely to damage a beginner's dissections than the unfamiliar scalpel. The probe should be blunt and should serve as an extension of the fingers. It is used to lift tissues, to push tissues aside in order to expose underlying structures, and to feel for tissues that cannot be readily seen. Both ends of the probe should be used. The blunt forceps handle also serves as an excellent probe. Wherever possible, the student should have available two forceps—a narrow-tipped one for close work and a broad-tipped one for gross studies. Forceps are used to hold and to lift tissues. They should be used for lifting whenever scissors are used for cutting. No part should ever be cut without first being raised; otherwise, underlying parts might be destroyed.

Dissection Techniques

The assistant should emphasize that dissecting does not mean "cutting up"; it means "exposing to view." Hence, nothing should ever be cut unless this is absolutely necessary to expose a part. The student should keep in mind that the more that is cut apart, the more the structural relationships among parts will be destroyed. Organizational patterns must always be preserved as much as possible. Where cutting cannot be avoided, the student must be sure that he has fully identified and studied the structural connections of a part before he cuts it. It may be valuable to make a quick, labeled sketch of a region before part of that region is cut.

The assistant should guide the student in observation of the following dissection pointers:

(1) Read directions carefully before beginning a dissection. Obey directions judiciously.

(2) Identify structures to be cut before actually cutting them.

(3) Lift all structures that are to be cut.

(4) Cut only what is necessary.

(5) Use probes and fingers carefully to expose structures to view.

(6) Proceed to study the exposed structures.

Observation Factors in Dissections

In carrying out a dissection, the student is primarily interested in observing, tracing, and establishing bounds and relationships of various named structures of the animal or human body. Some of these structures, such as the liver, are stationary; other structures, such as the ureter, are coursing structures which begin at Point A and pass to Point B along a certain route in the body.

In guiding the student's observations toward a comprehensive viewing and description of stationary and coursing structures in the laboratory, the assistant needs a set of specific observation questions or factors that should direct the observation of the structure so that the most comprehensive understanding of that structure as an anatomical part is developed. As the student dissects, probes, cleans, exposes, traces, and names structures in the laboratory, the following "observation factors" should be applied and discussed by the assistant with the student and his dissection partner while the students are actually working with the laboratory specimen. These observation factors should be mastered by the assistant; he may wish to duplicate the factors and make them available as general aids to dissection by his students. As answers are developed for each factor, the students should make their answers known to one another and to the assistant. They should write in their notebooks answers regarding observations for selected structures.

When all these observation factors have been determined, the student can feel that he has developed, under the assistant's guidance, a satisfactorily comprehensive anatomical description of (1) a stationary organ and (2) a coursing structure of the body.

The Stationary Structure

Describe or list the

  (1) Size of the organ—(a) length, (b) thickness, (c) width;
  (2) Shape;
  (3) Comparision with some familiar object, such as a balloon, pear, or apple;
  (4) Degree of firmness;
  (5) Color;
  (6) Edges or borders;
  (7) Surfaces;
  (8) Names of structures lying just above it;
  (9) Names of structures lying just below it;
 (10) Names of structures lying just in front of it;
 (11) Names of structures lying just behind it;
 (12) Names of structures lying just to the right of it;
 (13) Names of structures lying just to the left of it;
 (14) System or systems to which the organ belongs;
 (15) Functions of the organ;
 (16) Names of structures passing into the organ;
 (17) Names of structures passing out of the organ;
 (18) Names of structures passing through the organ;
 (19) Names of structures passing around the organ;
 (20) Names of structures lying in contact with the organ.

The Coursing Structure

Describe or list the

  (1) Beginning of the structure;
  (2) Ending of the structure;
  (3) Diameter of the structure;
  (4) Color;
  (5) Length;
  (6) Organs structure passes over in its course;
  (7) Organs structure passes under in its course;
  (8) Organs structure passes around in it course;
  (9) Organs structure passes through in its course;

(10) Organs lying in front of the structure;
(11) Organs lying behind the structure;
(12) Organs lying to the right of the structure;
(13) Organs lying to the left of the structure;
(14) System or systems to which structure belongs;
(15) Function or functions of the structure.

THE TERM PAPER

Many departments emphasize the production of term papers in various courses to stimulate acquaintance with the biological literature and with scientific journalism. Each student may be required to prepare an acceptable term paper and to meet a deadline for its completion. This deadline is usually made known to the students during the early or middle part of the course. The paper is generally evaluated by the professor in consultation with the assistant.

Nature and Purposes of the Term Paper

The biological science term paper is a written account of the student's individual and comprehensive investigation of a selected area of the biological field in which he has a special interest. The assistant is in good position to encourage interest and participation in term paper research.

The purposes of the term paper are: (1) to provide an opportunity for the student to do intensive study in a biological area especially appealing to him; (2) to express his initiative and perseverance in an avenue of learning outside the formal lecture and laboratory sessions; and (3) to gain experience in library research techniques.

The Term Paper Title

The student may select a title from a list of suggested titles presented to him by the assistant and compiled from the titles provided subsequently in this chapter. These titles could be duplicated or posted conveniently for viewing by students.

The student may also decide upon a title himself, with the approval of the assistant or professor. The student must select a title sufficiently narrow in scope to permit a logical attack upon his subject.

Materials and Supplies

1. Paper—good quality bond, lined or unlined, with or without hole punches
2. Typewriter or pen and ink
3. Index cards or notebook paper for research notes
4. Reference sources
5. Gem clips or stapler
6. Term paper cover, purchased or constructed by the student

Preparation Procedure

1. Select a title.
2. Obtain assistant's or professor's approval if title is other than titles suggested by the assistant.
3. Gather materials and supplies.
4. Do research, consulting all necessary sources of information and keeping notes on notebook paper or index cards.
5. Work on a regular schedule.
6. The paper content should show logical organization and arrangement of topics and subtopics.
7. The purpose of the paper should be clearly stated near the beginning.
8. The length of the paper will generally be no less than 2700 or more than 3000 words; the length may vary within wide limits.
9. The general principles of English grammatical usage must be followed throughout.
10. The paper must be legibly written or printed in ink, or typewritten.
11. Diagrams, neatly and accurately labeled, may be used in the body of the paper to illustrate points.
12. Each page should be numbered except index pages, bibliography, reference citation pages, and the first page of the body of the paper.
13. Only one side of each sheet may be used.
14. The paper must be written and rewritten several times, with the student trying to improve each time. The assistant must emphasize this requirement to the student.
15. Footnotes may or may not be required, but direct quotations should always have their sources acknowledged.
16. At the end of the paper a section entitled "References Cited" should appear—a numbered list of sources consulted, alphabetically arranged by author, with name of book or article, date and place of pub-

lication, number of pages in the book or the numbered pages consulted in the magazine, pamphlet, or encyclopedia.

17. A comprehensive index of topics and subtopics and the pages on which these appear in the paper should be placed near the beginning of the paper.

18. The paper must be handed in on the date announced by the assistant, accompanied by all term paper notes taken during research on the paper.

19. The student must be prepared to hand in progress reports on the paper when these are called for by the assistant.

Criteria for Evaluation

1. Comprehensiveness and degree of accomplishment of the student's stated purpose,

2. Logical organization of subject matter,

3. Observation of deadline (many professors will not accept late papers),

4. Spelling, punctuation, and grammar,

5. Quality of progress reports handed in periodically when called for by the assistant,

6. Difficulty of the subject chosen.

SEMESTER DEMONSTRATION PROJECT AND EXHIBIT PREPARATION

Various departments of biology require that some type of student term demonstration project or exhibit be submitted for credit in particular courses. When properly motivated and supervised, project work can be extremely stimulating and beneficial.

General Nature of the Project

While details of projects differ from school to school and from professor to professor, the project or exhibit is generally a teaching aid or mechanical or audio-visual device such as a poster, chart, scrapbook, model, graph, flannel board, or other preparation of the student's choice that may be used to illustrate an idea gained from lectures, readings, demonstrations, laboratory sessions, or campus discussions concerning some phase of biological science that has been treated during the course. The assistant is in position to encourage interest in such work and to supply guidance as the students pursue this requirement.

Purposes of the Project

1. To test the initiative, sincerity, and perseverence of the student in an avenue other than the purely scholastic,

2. To give the student opportunity for expression of his originality and creativity,

3. To offer opportunity for research and original investigation,

4. To offer the student the opportunity to use his hands and demonstrate his manual dexterity,

5. To help discover hidden interests and talents among a student group,

6. To help the student to apply in a practical way the knowledge gained from the course,

7. To provide displays and exhibits for use within the department as a means of encouraging other students in the project method.

The Project Title

1. Each student should select a title from the list of proposed term demonstration projects that appears subsequently in this chapter. These may be duplicated by the assistant and made available to the class.

2. The title selected should be especially appealing to the student.

3. The student may prefer to select a title other than those provided. The title should have the approval of the assistant or professor if it is different from those on the suggested list.

4. The project may fall within the same field as the term paper and may be used to illustrate points of the term paper when both project and term paper are required.

Materials and Preparation Supplies

1. A variety of illustrative materials and equipment, such as cardboard, crayons, paints, pictures, clay, cloth, yarn, wood, metal, plastic, wire, rubber, thread, cord, sponge, glass, pins, paper, or other materials of the student's choice, may be used in an original way to vividly stress some special topic of the biology course experience. Each student will supply his own materials.

2. Purchase of expensive materials is not necessary. The assistant should request that investment in the project not exceed one or two dollars.

Appearance of the Project

1. The project should tell a complete biological story upon first observation.

2. The project must appear neat, with attractive spatial arrangement of its parts.

3. Writing, printing, typing, and lettering should be carefully executed, with attention to correct spelling.

Procedure in Project Preparation

1. At a time selected by the assistant or professor, the student should select a title.

2. Obtain the professor's approval of title choice if the selected title is other than one of the titles presented to him by the assistant.

3. Gather necessary materials and equipment and conduct research and investigation.

4. Plan the general appearance of the project and decide upon spatial arrangement, measurements, and lettering.

5. Work on a regular schedule.

6. Prepare to make progress reports on the state of the project's preparation when these progress reports are called for by the assistant or professor.

7. Work toward the deadline for handing in the project for the professor's final evaluation. This deadline will be announced by the assistant after consultation with the professor.

8. Consult with the assistant when any problem arises during project preparation.

Evaluation Criteria

The assistant will aid the professor in the final evaluation of the project. Criteria of evaluation include:

1. Amount of time and research;
2. Originality;
3. Student initiative;
4. Neatness;
5. General appearance and teaching value of the project;
6. Spelling;
7. Quality of progress reports;
8. Difficulty of the project undertaken.

SUGGESTED TITLES FOR ORAL OR WRITTEN
READING REPORTS, PAPERS, OR
DEMONSTRATION PROJECTS

Areas of term paper and project interest generally include (1) the various systems of the animal body, including the human, and (2) topics in general plant and animal biology.

Integumentary System

1. Skin disorders of childhood
2. Maintaining a healthy skin
3. Drug allergies denoted by skin changes
4. A program of education in care of the skin
5. Skin changes in selected diseases
6. Prevention and cure of acne
7. The skin in relation to the external environment
8. The hair and skin of lower animal forms
9. The mechanism of inheritance of skin color
10. Skin color and its social implications
11. Truth of advertisements of skin beauty aids
12. Skin structure
13. A detailed study of the various skin functions
14. Record of daily care of skin over a two-month period
15. First aid for skin injuries
16. Record of interview with dermatologist
17. Mechanism of hair growth and pigmentation
18. The skin as a barrier against disease organisms
19. Nature and importance of skin elasticity
20. Skin changes with age

Muscular System

1. Chemical aspects of muscular reactions
2. Nature of a hereditary muscular disease
3. Maintaining a healthy heart muscle
4. Daily exercise and diet in muscular conditioning
5. Muscular strength and weakness
6. Embryonic origin and development of the muscular system
7. Rigor mortis and muscular changes after death
8. A study of muscular disorders
9. Comparative means of locomotion
10. Muscular bellies, origins, and insertions
11. Types of muscular tissue

12. Laboratory procedures in studying muscle action
13. Functional relation of the muscular system to the skeletal system
14. Muscular injuries in wartime
15. The muscles of the frog and man
16. Muscular conditioning through calisthenics
17. Mechanics of posture control

Skeletal System

1. A study of changes in cranial size through evolution
2. The Haversian system
3. Types of fractures and methods of treatment
4. Changes in the skeletal system with age
5. Rickets
6. Parathyroids in calcium and phosphorus metabolism
7. The diet and skeletal system
8. A study of joint diseases
9. The nature of cartilage
10. The relation of bone to muscles and nerves
11. How a bone grows
12. The gross and microscopic anatomy of bone
13. Skeletal system disorders
14. The functional importance of hand structure and movements
15. Cartilage, growth, and ossification

Digestive System

1. The mechanism of peptic ulcer production
2. A program of community education on proper diet and nutrition
3. Calories, work, and recreation
4. Physical processes involved in absorption
5. Feeding body cells
6. Endocrine and nervous control of the digestive process
7. Disorders of the digestive system
8. Truth of advertisements for reducing aids
9. The mechanism of carbohydrate digestion
10. Graphs on incidence and nature of digestive disorders
11. Models of teeth, tongue, and salivary glands
12. The endocrines in digestion
13. Tube-within-a-tube type of body organization
14. Illustration of production mechanism of five digestive disorders
15. Comparative study of digestive tract of man and lower animal forms

Circulatory System

1. Surgical techniques in treating heart defects
2. Nervous and chemical control of the heart rate
3. Disorders of the heart and circulation in childhood
4. Maintaining a healthy circulatory system
5. The nature and importance of blood pressure
6. The heart and recreation
7. Economic aspects of circulatory system disorders
8. Prevalence of circulatory diseases in various world societies
9. The life span and circulation
10. Drugs used in treating circulatory diseases
11. Life and work of Robert Adams (1791-1875)
12. Life and work of William Harvey (1578-1657)
13. Life and work of Edward Jenner (1749-1823)
14. Life and work of Ernest Henry Starling (1866-1927)
15. A mechanism to illustrate the physiology of the failing heart
16. Surgical techniques for the failing heart
17. First aid treatment for circulatory disturbances
18. The healthy heart
19. Comparative study of the hearts of different animals
20. The physical work done by the heart
21. Exhibit of drugs used in treating circulatory diseases
22. The mechanics of high blood pressure
23. Relation of the circulatory system to other body systems
24. Mechanism of production of the enlarged heart
25. Why swelling occurs with heart trouble

Respiratory System

1. Respiratory disease as a family problem
2. Research on the common cold
3. Annual economic losses through respiratory disease
4. Importance of a healthy respiratory system in physical education activities
5. Chemical and physical aspects of respiration
6. Comparative study of respiration in selected lower animals and man
7. Respiratory hazards among miners
8. Relation of the respiratory system to other body systems
9. Methods of air conditioning and purification
10. Physical processes of inspiration and expiration

11. Physical process of gaseous exchange in the lungs
12. Illustration of lung damage in respiratory disease
13. Various skull sinuses and mechanics of their inflammation
14. Regions of spread of the common cold
15. Sectional views of the organs of respiration
16. Plant respiration in relation to animal respiration

Endocrine System

1. Historical studies in endocrinology
2. The use of hormones in treating the physically and mentally diseased
3. A detailed study of diabetes mellitus
4. The pituitary as the master gland
5. The chemistry of body adjustment for emergencies
6. The hormonal control of the reproductive processes
7. The mysteries of growth and the relation of hormones to this process
8. The nature and variety of synthetic hormones
9. The relation between the nervous system and the endocrine system
10. The hormones in normal and in abnormal metabolism
11. Detailed microscopic structure of selected endocrine glands
12. Methods of endocrine research
13. Demonstration of chemical structure and actions of ten different hormones
14. Tests for pregnancy
15. Hormones in relation to the aging process
16. The hormones in childbirth
17. Details of a basal metabolism test
18. Illustration of surgical techniques in endocrinology

Excretory System

1. Selected disorders of the urinary system
2. Physical and chemical nature of materials appearing in the urine
3. Detailed structure and function of the rectum
4. The mechanism of kidney stone production and treatment
5. The life and work of Marcello Malpighi (1628-1694)
6. Ranking excretory system diseases with other diseases as causes of death
7. How to maintain a healthy excretory system

Reproductive System

1. Importance of a knowledge of reproductive physiology in family living
2. Juvenile syphilis
3. Emphasis given to sex education in the public schools
4. An effective method of teaching reproduction to the elementary child
5. Problems of pregnancy
6. Statistical study of venereal disease in the United States
7. Man-hour losses from venereal disease
8. The venereal disease problem in the armed forces
9. The development of male and female reproductive systems
10. A study of changing birth rates among different nations
11. Religious teachings concerning reproduction in family relations
12. Kinds and costs of drug treatment in venereal disease
13. Development of selected body systems
14. Population control and birth rates of different world societies
15. The details of structure of the pregnant uterus
16. Exhibit of types of ectopic pregnancy
17. Mechanical model demonstrating physical processes of parturition
18. Demonstration of ligaments anchoring the uterus
19. Mechanics of ductless glandular control of the menstrual cycle
20. The nature and importance of the chromosomes
21. Experimental work in heredity
22. Sex inheritance
23. Mechanisms of producing mutations
24. Inheritance of specific human characteristics
25. Heredity and evolution
26. Economic aspects of genetics
27. Transmission of selected dominant and recessive traits
28. The albino
29. Physical and chemical structure of chromosomes
30. Spermatogenesis
31. Transmission of hereditary traits
32. Research problems in genetics
33. Genetic aspects of albinism
34. Economic aspects of heredity and genetics
35. Summary descriptions of pamphlets on government work in genetics

36. Nature and importance of genes in heredity
37. Effects of atomic and hydrogen bomb radiations
38. Interview of government or university geneticist
39. Leaders in development of eugenics thought
40. Proposed methods in a eugenics program
41. Sterilization as a eugenics procedure
42. Types of mental deficiency
43. Eugenics aspects of struggle for existence in human society
44. A program of community education in eugenics
45. Inheritance and eugenics
46. A study of the inherited disorders of body systems
47. Present knowledge and application of principles of human heredity
48. Structure and nature of the nucleus of egg and sperm
49. Methods of eugenics control in society
50. Eugenics as a debatable issue
51. Record of daily observations of a mentally deficient child
52. Original graphs of incidence of heritable mental and physical disorders in the United States

Nervous System

1. The nervous control of digestion
2. Nervous system injuries in athletics
3. The care of the mentally diseased in various countries
4. A history of the mental hygiene movement
5. The development of the nervous system
6. A study of the importance of various reflexes
7. Surgical treatments for nervous system disorders
8. A study of inherited mental disorders
9. Annual costs of care of the mentally deficient
10. The initiation and execution of voluntary movements
11. Advances made in care of the mentally diseased
12. Surgical techniques in brain disorders
13. Original graphs of numbers of mentally and emotionally diseased in U.S. over ten-year period
14. Nervous system damage by syphilis
15. Cooperative function of parasympathetic and sympathetic nervous systems
16. Nervous system control of other body systems

Special Senses System

1. Common disorders of the eye
2. Corneal transplants
3. Proper care of the eyes
4. Muscular and nervous control of the eye
5. Hearing acuity in man and lower animal forms
6. Mechanism of color blindness
7. Interrelationship of taste and smell
8. Kinesthetic sense
9. Importance of nerve endings of the skin
10. Eye and ear diseases
11. Mechanisms of production of five common ear ailments
12. Mechanism of sensory paralyses
13. Mechanism of hearing and equilibrium maintenance
14. Original graphs of incidence of eye and ear disease
15. Recent advances in treatment of ear disorders
16. Mechanism of cold, heat, pressure, and pain sensation
17. Explanation of the sense of smell

General Biology Titles

1. A study of leaf growth
2. A model greenhouse
3. Common insects
4. Common weeds
5. Corn products
6. Division of labor in the animal kingdom
7. Plant life in forests
8. Sources and biological uses of plastic and rubber
9. Scientific methods of farming
10. Conservation and land erosion
11. Blood vessel systems
12. Effects of mineral deficiencies on corn
13. Inversion loop in chromosome pairing
14. Effects of crilium on plant growth
15. Steps in soybean processing
16. The cell structure of various leaves
17. Food value of cereals
18. Some effects of molds and their products on plants
19. The effects of nutrients on algae
20. The effects of colored lights on plant growth

21. Individuality in nature
22. Structural differences between organic and inorganic matter
23. Genetic effects of X-Rays on *Drosophila*
24. Dental caries and heredity
25. A study of the poison of the short-tailed shrew
26. Effects of nicotine on rabbits
27. Conditions under which progressive osmosis occurs
28. Effects of tranquilizers on the metabolic rate of white mice
29. Survival in a closed atmoshpere

THE ROLE OF THE ASSISTANT IN PROVIDING
BASIC OR FRONTIER RESEARCH IDEAS

Many persons are drawn into careers in the biological sciences because of the opportunity to explore unmapped territory. The following fifty suggested topics are presented to the assistant so that he may have a part in directing the especially curious student into areas as yet not carefully investigated. These ideas should help the assistant to stimulate the imagination and excite the research interest of his students.

These students should be able to learn enough background facts regarding these topics to scout out at least a small corner of new territory. This is the type of experience that is not soon forgotten.

Suggested Areas for Investigation

1. Maintaining the balance between growth and death of tissue cells
2. Explaining the migration of birds
3. Exceptional human perception, bat radar, and the homing instinct of pigeons
4. The significance of the thickness of leaves of plants
5. The chemical "time clocks" of cells
6. Lithosperm and the secretion of sex hormones in animals
7. The search for microbes that will refine oil
8. Equipment and systems for comparing life on earth with life on other planets
9. Testing cellulose to determine if a living thing is plant or animal
10. Slime molds as clues to the formation of cell types and the process of cell differentiation
11. The importance of photosynthesis to the balanced aquarium
12. Devising an economical method for harvesting algae

13. Lawns that need no mowing and dwarf trees that yield normal-sized fruit

14. Treating sick plants with pills to combat their diseases

15. Ethyl alcohol as a stimulant to the growth of algae and seedlings

16. Developing tropical areas into major food producers

17. An antiseptic varnish for combating fungus growth in trees

18. Whether riboflavin, adenine, and gibberellic acid produce heat resistance in plants

19. Plant production of serum containing antibodies when injected with human red blood cells

20. Globulins of skim milk to halt destructive effects of a plant virus in tobacco, pepper, and tomato plants.

21. A program for eradication of the imported fire ant

22. Modern organic insecticides against the boll weevil, boll worm, and cotton flea hopper

23. A radio-frequency electric field for destruction of insects which damage stored wheat

24. The differences between centipedes and millepedes as to structure and life habits

25. The causes of the schooling behavior of fish

26. The six mammals in danger of extinction

27. The hereditary basis for the song features of birds

28. Seasonal studies of size changes in the skull of the common shrew

29. The process of hibernation and related "slowdowns"

30. The biological motivation and function of head-scratching in birds

31. An analysis of royal jelly

32. Clinical use of a plastic polyurethane foam for treating leg fractures

33. Skin transplants with young tadpoles and implications for humans

34. Protection against contamination from radioactive fallout

35. Lamp-produced negative air ions to improve human health and needs

36. Electronic substitutes for various body organs

37. The role of RNA in skin grafts

38. The advantages and disadvantages of using cadaver blood in transfusions

39. The effects of saliva on teeth

40. The electron microscope and teeth-and-bone-seeking radioisotopes in dentistry

41. Better fillings for front teeth

42. The causes of gingivitis and pyorrhea
43. The hereditary process in tooth conditions of man
44. The relation of studies of the human brain to the production of better computers
45. Humor as a safety valve for hospital patients
46. The perception of depth on the part of creeping babies
47. The faster beat of the human heart caused by electric shock
48. Consciousness and the reasons for its existence
49. A sense of humor among dogs
50. The nature of the human aging process

CLASSIFICATION OUTLINES FOR THE ASSISTANT'S APPLICATION WITH STUDENTS

Students who are enrolled in biology courses and professors who are engaged in various types of research are often interested in determining the scientific name and taxonomic relationship of various plant and animal forms. Such forms may be found during field trips, or they may be brought into the department from time to time as students explore their environment.

Plant and animal identification and determination of class, order, family, genus, and species are specialized areas of biological knowledge and skill. The broad elementary outlines of the plant and animal kingdoms presented in the following sections will aid the assistant as he helps students to become accustomed to the concept and meaning of phylum, class, order, genus, and species.

Plant Kingdom Classification Outline
Subkingdom 1. Thallophyta
Plants have neither roots nor leaves. The undifferentiated plant body has no phloem or xylem vascular tissue.
Division 1. Chlorophyta (green algae)
Plant body with pigments contained in plastids; unicellular and multicellular species; colonial and solitary; motile; nonmotile; asexual and sexual reproduction; habitat: fresh and salt water; food stored as starch.
Division 2. Cyanophyta (blue-green algae)
Plants without definite nucleus; chlorophyll not contained in plastids; contain phycocyanin, a blue-green pigment; asexual repro-

duction; nonmotile; unicellular or colonial; fresh and salt water, damp rocks and soil.

Division 3. Euglenophyta (euglenoids)

One-celled organisms exhibiting some characteristics of both plants and animals; plastids contain chlorophyll; movement by flagella; reproduction by fission and cysts; no cell wall; primarily fresh water.

Division 4. Chrysophyta (yellow-green, golden-brown algae and diatoms)

Color by pigments xanthophyll and carotene; carbohydrates stored as oils; motile and nonmotile; filamentous and nonfilamentous bodies; fresh water, marine, and on soil.

Division 5. Pyrrophyta

Dinoflagellata the most numerous and common class; food stored as oil or as starch; plastids golden brown or yellow-green; cell walls with furrows containing flagella; reproduction commonly asexual; usually marine.

Division 6. Phaeophyta (brown algae)

Characteristic color due to brown pigment fucoxanthin; pigment contained in plastids; food stored as oil or carbohydrate; asexual reproduction by motile zoospores; sexual reproduction isogamous and oogamous; nonmotile; mostly marine.

Division 7. Rhodophyta (red algae)

Characteristic red color due to phycoerythrin; food stored as starch; reproduce sexually; gametes nonmotile; mostly marine.

Division 8. Schizophyta (thallophytes without chlorophyll)

Unicellular; asexual reproduction by cell division.

Order 1. Eubacteriales

True bacteria

Order 2. Actinomycetales

Threadlike plants; reproduction by cell division or conidia.

Division 9. Myxomycophyta (slime molds and fungi)

Plant appears as mass of protoplasm; spores do not form hyphae.

Division 10. Eumycophyta (true fungi)

Characteristic hyphae compose the plant body.

Class 1. Phycomycetes (algal fungi)

Hyphae without cross walls; reproduction by zygospores and oospores.

Class 2. Ascomycetes (sac fungi)
Hyphae with cross walls; sexual fusion forms ascospores.
Class 3. Basidiomycetes (club fungi)
Basidiospores
Class 4. Fungi Imperfecti
Asexual reproduction
Subkingdom 2. Embryophyta
Zygote develops within archegonium or in embryo sac.
Division 11. Bryophyta
Dominant gametophyte generation with attached sporophyte;
no vascular tissue; multicellular archegonia and antheridia.
Class 1. Hepaticae (liverworts)
Thalluslike or leaflike plant body; inconspicuous sporophyte
generation; spore capsule opening irregularly or by valves.
Class 2. Anthocerotae (hornworts)
Thalluslike gametophyte; sporophyte elongated and cylin-
drical with basal meristem; capsule opens by two valves.
Class 3. Musci (mosses)
Prostrate and erect; long-lived gametophyte; spore capsule
with iid.
Division 12. Tracheophyta
Dominant sporophyte; vascular tissue present; archegonia pres-
ent in all except angiosperms.
Subdivision A. Psilopsida
Plants usually without leaves or roots; terminal sporangia;
four known species.
Subdivision B. Lycopsida
Plants with small, simple leaves; sporangia usually on dif-
ferentiated strobilus; stems without joints; leaf gaps absent.
Order 1. Lepidodendrales (giant club mosses)
Sigillaria
Order 2. Lycopodiales (club mosses)
Lycopodium
Order 3. Selaginellales (small club mosses)
Selaginella
Order 4. Isoetales (quillworts)
Isoetes

Subdivision C. Sphenopsida
Leaves small; jointed stems; sporangia on modified sporo-
phylls; known mostly as fossils.
   Order 1. Sphenophyllales
       Sphenophyllum
   Order 2. Equisetales (horsetails)
       Equisetum
Subdivision D. Pteropsida
Complex leaves, sporangia, or sporophylls; leaf gaps.
   Class 1. Filicinae (ferns)
   Many sporangia usually on undersurface of leaf; motile
sperm.
      Order 1. Ophioglossales (adder's tongue)
      Order 2. Filicales (typical ferns)
   Class 2. Gymnospermae
   Naked seed
      Order 1. Pteridospermae (seed ferns)
      Seed-bearing plants; seeds borne on leaves.
      Order 2. Cycadales
      Reproductive structures usually in cones; motile sperms.
      Order 3. Ginkgoales
      One species, *Ginkgo biloba*
      Order 4. Coniferales (the conifers)
      Evergreens with leaves modified into needles; reproduc-
tive structures enclosed in cones; pollen tube for sperm
transport; sperm non-motile.
   Class 3. Angiospermae (the flowering plants)
   Seeds enclosed by carpels; broad leaves; sperm transfer by
pollen tube.
      Subclass A. Dicotyledonae
      Plants with two seed leaves; leaves with netted veins;
flower parts in four's and five's; vascular tissue in definite
arrangement due to presence of organized cambium.
      Subclass B. Monocotyledonae
      Plants with one seed leaf; flower parts in three's; vascular
tissue scattered due to the absence of organized cambium
area; leaves with parallel venation; mostly herbaceous.

Animal Kingdom Classification Outline
Section 1. Animal unicellular
  Phylum 1. Protozoa; Class Sarcodina (*sar-ko-di-na*)
    Move by means of pseudopodia (Sarcodina) (*Amoeba*)
                            (*Pelomyxa*)
    Special Characteristics
    Protoplasmic pseudopodia for locomotion and ingestion of food; flowing protoplasm produces constantly changing shape; free-living in fresh and salt water; also parasitic forms; reproduce by binary fission; one to several nuclei.
  Phylum 1. Protozoa; Class Mastigophora (*mas-ti-gof'o-ra*)
    Move by means of one or more flagella
                (Mastigophora)
                (*Euglena*)
                (*Volvox*)
    Special Characteristics
    Move by means of flagella; commonly known as flagellates; some species contain chlorophyll and chlorophyll plastids; free-living in fresh and salt water; some parasitic; solitary and colonial; reproduction by encystment, binary fission, sex cells, and parthenogenesis.
  Phylum 1. Protozoa; Class Ciliata
    Move by means of cilia (Cilata) (*Paramecium*)
                         (*Spirostomum*)
    Special Characteristics
    Move by means of cilia; commonly called ciliates; many forms found in grass-infusion cultures; parasitic and free-living; reproduction by binary fission, conjugation, autogamy.
  Phylum 1. Protozoa; Class Sporozoa (*spo-ro-zo'-a*)
    Nonmotile adult parasites reproducing by means of spores
                        (Sporozoa)
                        (*Monocystis*)
                        (*Plasmodium*)
    Special Characteristics
    No locomotor organelles in adult, but all are motile at some stage in life cycle; no mouth or vacuoles; all are parasites with complex life cycles.

Section II. Animal multicellular

   Phylum 2.   Porifera; Class Calcispongiae

      Skeleton of monaxon or tetraxon (four-rayed) calcareous spicules (Calcispongiae) (*Grantia*) (*Leucosolenia*) (*Scypha*)

     Special Characteristics

      Skeleton of calcareous spicules either one-rayed (monaxon), three-rayed, or four-rayed (tetraxon); pores and canals of either the ascon or sycon type; shallow fresh and salt water; Calcispongiae or Calcarea class names used synonymously.

   Phylum 2.   Porifera; Class Hyalospongiae

      Skeleton of hexaxon (six-rayed), siliceous spicules

                         (Hyalospongiae)

                         (Sand and glass sponges)

                         (Venus' flower basket)

     Special Characteristics

      Spicules are white and like spun glass; often called glass sponges.

   Phylum 2.   Porifera; Class Demospongiae

      Skeleton of spongin alone, spicules, or no skeleton

                         (Demospongiae)

                         (Commercial sponges)

                         (*Spongilla*)

     Special Characteristics

      Frequently large and brilliantly colored; complex canal system; mostly marine.

   Phylum 3.   Coelenterata; Class Hydrozoa (hi-dro-zo'-a)

      Radial symmetry; gastrovascular cavity without partitions; polyp stage solitary or colonial, free-swimming medusa with a velum

          (Hydrozoa)

          (*Hydra*)

          (*Obelia*)

          (*Gonionemus*)

     Special Characteristics

      No true gullet or stomadeum; sex cells discharged directly to outside; certain species demonstrate alternation of generations.

Phylum 3. Coelenterata; Class Scyphozoa (*si-fo-zo'-a*)
Solitary; usually free-floating; small to large medusa with middle mesoglea comprising primary body mass; no velum
(Scyphozoa)
(Aurelia)
Special Characteristics
Gastrovascular cavity held in place by membranous mesenteries: all carnivorous and marine; size range from one inch to four feet in diameter.
Phylum 3. Coelenterata; Class Anthozoa (*an-tho-zo'a*)
Solitary or colonial (coral); polyps with tentacles; enteron divided by mesenteries; corals secrete a limy skeleton; sexual reproduction; dioecious; planula larvae; marine; cellular mesoglea
(Anthozoa)
(Metridium)
(Corals)
Special Characteristics
Well-developed stomadeum; most polyps produce colony by budding; gullet fastened to body wall by number of radially arranged membranous mesenteries.
Section III. Animals with bilateral symmetry; well-defined organs and systems; usually complete digestive tract; coelom usually present.
Phylum 4. Platyhelminthes; Class Turbellaria
Triploblastic; branched digestive system; body flat, soft, wormlike; free-living; body covered with ciliated epidermis with mucous glands; no suckers or hooks; ventral mouth and branched digestive tract; often colored (Turbellaria) (*Dugesia tigrina*)
Special Characteristics
Fresh and salt water and soil; special ectodermal cells called *rhabdites* for defense; eyespots and auricles; high powers of regeneration; shows cephalization.
Phylum 5. Platyhelminthes: Class Trematoda
Epidermis with cuticle but no cilia; all parasitic
(Termatoda) (liver fluke)
(*Fasciola hepatica*)
Special Characteristics
Ventral sucker or hooks or both; leaf-shaped, two-branched digestive tract.

Phylum 5. Platyhelminthes; Class Cestoda (ses-toe'-da)

Parasites; cuticle but no cilia; suckers or hooks or both; body flat, elongate with anterior scolex and proglottids; no digestive tract. (Cestoda) (tapeworms) (*Taenia*)

Special Characteristics

No cilia on the ectoderm of adults; endoparasites in higher animals at some stages of their life cycle; proglottids (pseudo-segments), each with complete reproductive organs; no mouth or digestive tract.

Phylum 6. Aschelminthes; Class Nematoda

Pseudocoelomata: Spaces between organs; coelom without lining (false coelom); complete digestive tract (Nematoda)
(*Ascaris*)
(*Trichinella*)
(*Necator*)

Special Characteristics

Body elongated, round and unsegmented; lateral lines with excretory canal; straight digestive tract with mouth and anus; anterior nerve ring with six cords; dioecious.

Phylum 6. Aschelminthes; Class Nematoda; Order Spirurida
(Filarial worms) (*Wuchereria
bancrofti*)

Special Characteristics

The parasites in higher animals characterized by intermediate insect host; esophagus with two regions; the anterior portion is muscular, the posterior is glandular.

Phylum 6. Aschelminthes; Class Rotifera

Often called "wheel animals"; anterior end with cilia-bearing discs; body with trunk and tail; adhesive glands for attachment; males minute (Class Rotifera)

Special Characteristics

Plentiful in fresh water; few in sea; internal organs include several systems; little difference between trocophore larva and adult.

Phylum 7. Acanthocephala

Flat, rough worms with no intestines; parasitic
(Spiny-headed worms)
(*Neoechinorynchus*)

Special Characteristics

Central nervous system composed of single ganglionic mass; retractible spiny proboscis; larva in arthropods; adults in vertebrates.

Phylum 8. Mollusca; Class Amphineura

Bilateral symmetry; shell of eight parts; inconspicuous head, without tentacles; marine; calcareous dorsal plates

(Amphineura) (chitons)

Special Characteristics

Body comprised of a series of eight calcerous dorsal plates; inconspicuous head; gills for respiration; bilateral symmetry; marine.

Phylum 8. Mollusca; Class Gastropoda (gas-trop'-o-da)

Muscular foot; distinct head with one or two pairs of tentacles; radula; viscera contained in a coiled, calcerous shell; some species have no shell; land and water

(Gastropoda) (Snails, slugs, whelks)
(Limax) (Mures) (Conus)

Special Characteristics

Body usually more or less spirally coiled with part of the digestive system in the flat, muscular foot; distinct head with sensory tentacles; gills or pulmonary lungs are respiratory structures; calcareous shell (if present) is coiled; head and foot usually asymmetrical; filelike radula.

Phylum 8. Mollusca; Class Scaphopoda (ska-fop'-o-da)

Body with hollow, toothlike shell, open at either end

(Scaphopoda) (tooth shells)
(Dentalium)

Special Characteristics

Elongated, marine mollusks; three-lobed foot; calcareous shell secreted by the mantle; head reduced; bilateral symmetry; no gills.

Phylum 8. Mollusca; Class Cephalopoda (sef-al-op'-o-da)

Foot modified; mouth with arms and tentacles; head with complex eyes; shell reduced, or absent, or internal; marine

(Cephalopoda) (squid) (octopus) (cuttlefish) (Nautilus)

Special Characteristics

Head and foot fused; mouth with tentacles, which may contain suckers; bilateral symmetry (externally); shell reduced internally or absent; one or two pairs of gills; head with well-developed nervous system; siphon for expelling water; ink sac for defense.

Phylum 8. Mollusca; Class Pelecypoda (*pel-e-sip'-o-da*)

Bivalve shell, secreted by mouth; hatchet-shaped foot; no head tentacles, eyes or radula (Pelecypoda) (mussels, oysters, scallops, "shipworms") (*Toredo*)

Special Characteristics

The muscular foot extends between valves for locomotion; calcareous shell with paired lateral valves secreted by mantle; gills paired and lateral; viscera contained in foot; bilateral symmetry; all aquatic; many are marine; no head, eyes, tentacles, or radula.

Phylum 9. Annelida; Class Polychaeta (*poli-ke'-ta*)

Parapodia with bristlelike setae; definite head region with tentacles; mostly marine; usually dioecious; conspicuous segments; no suckers (Polychaeta) (Sand worm) (*Nereis*)

Special Characteristics

Marine worms having setae on parapodia; definite head region with tentacles; trocophore larva is free-swimming and ciliated; dioecious with sex organs appearing during breeding season.

Phylum 9. Annelida; Class Oligochaeta (*ol-i-go-ke'-ta*)

Bristlelike setae, few per somite; wormlike body with conspicuous segmentation; well-defined coelom

(Oligochaeta) (earthworms) (*Lumbricus*)

Special Characteristics

Fresh water and soil; few setae per segment; without head; no larval stage; hermaphroditic, but cross fertilization; excretion by nephridia; closed circulatory system with dorsal and ventral blood vessels.

Phylum 9. Annelida; Class Hirudinea (*hir-u-din-e-a*)

No setae or parapodia; body segmented, but segments inconspicuous; body flat and divided into external annuli; suckers present, a large posterior one, sometimes smaller anterior; hermaphroditic (Hirudinea) (Leeches) (*Hirudo*)

Special Characteristics

Flat body; sucker for attachment; no setae or parapodia; reduced coelom; hermaphroditic.

Phylum 10. Arthropoda; Class Crustacea (krus-ta'-she-a)

Body of two or three parts; chitinous exoskeleton; aquatic; head with two pairs of antennae, one pair of jaws; two pairs of maxillae; a variable number of segments; biramous appendages; respiration usually by gills

(Crustacea) (lobsters, crayfish, barnacles, crabs, water fleas)

Special Characteristics

Few species parasitic; numerous legs; body of head, thorax, and abdomen; head and thorax may be fused into a cephalothorax.

Phylum 10. Arthropoda; Class Myriapoda

Body with two parts; one pair of antennae; one pair of mandibles; one or two pairs of walking legs per somite; terrestrial

(Myriapoda) (Centipedes)

Special Characteristics

Long, slender bodies flattened dorsoventrally; 15 to 173 segments; swift moving; no wings; air breathing.

Phylum 10. Arthropoda; Class Insecta

Body of head, thorax, and abdomen; many species harmful; wings, if present, attached to thorax; chewing, sucking, or lapping mouth parts (Insecta) (bees, wasps, flies, beetles, etc.)

Special Characteristics

Certain species have wings at certain stages of their lives and not at others; few species are beneficial; as far as known most species are neither harmful nor beneficial.

Phylum 10. Arthropoda; Subphylum Chelicerata

Trachea-breathing or lung books or gill books; no antennae; body divided into cephalothorax and abdomen; four pairs of legs; chelicera; pedipalps (Arachnida) (spiders, scorpions, mites, ticks, harvestmen, king crabs)

Special Characteristics

No wings; no mandibles; one pair of nippers; no true jaws; terrestrial; some species detrimental; few species harmful; most species neither harmful nor helpful.

Phylum 11. Echinodermata; Class Asteroidea

Body typically in five parts; central disc with arms; dioecious; ambulacral groove on oral surface with protruding tube feet (Asteroidea) (starfish)

Special Characteristics

Free-living; five-rayed body, not sharply distinct from central disc; ambulacral groove on oral side of arms with tube feet, which are attached to water-vascular system; madreporite entrance to water vascular system; anus on aboral side of body, external pedicellariae.

Phylum 11. Echinodermata; Class Ophiuroidea (of-i-u-roid'-ea)

Typically pentamerous; slender distinct arms; no ambulacral grooves or anus; two rows of tube feet (Ophiuroidea) (brittle stars) (serpent stars)

Special Characteristics

Typically, free-living five rays; distinct central disk; no ambulacral grooves; madreporite on aboral side; no anus; two rows of tube feet without suckers or ampulla; five bursae around mouth for respiration; skeleton composed of solid round ossicles.

Phylum 11. Echinodermata; Class Echinoidea (ek-i-noid'-e-a)

Typically pentamerous without free arms; body is cylindrical, oval, or disc-shaped; skeleton of rows of fused plates

(Echinoidea) (sea urchins, sand dollars)

Special Characteristics

Body round, oval, or disc-shaped; body enclosed in shell of ten double-rowed calcareous plates; tube feet in five ambulacral regions; stalked pedicellariae; mouth surrounded by five teeth and ten gills.

Phylum 11. Echinodermata; Class Holothurioidea (hol-o-thu-ri-oid'-e-a)

Body is ovoid; sometimes cylindrical, muscular, and soft; no arms or pedicellariae; complete digestive tract with anterior mouth and posterior anus (Holothurioidea) (sea cucumbers)

Special Characteristics

Soft, ovoid to elongate muscular body; skeleton of microscopic ossicles; branched contractile tentacles around the mouth (modified tube feet); no external spines; madreporite in coelom; respiration by respiratory trees.

Phylum 11. Echinodermata; Class Crinoidea

Branched arms and flower-like body; usually aboral stalk for attachment (Crinoidea) (sea lilies, feather stars)

Special Characteristics

Body composed of limy plates with forked arms; featherlike pennules; mouth and anus on oral surface; each arm with ambulacral grooves and tentacle-like tube feet; no madreporite; reduced coelom; some attached by aboral stalk.

Phylum 12. Chordata; Subphylum Hemichordata
(hem-i-kor-da'-ta)

Wormlike animal; usually with proboscis and collar; notochord anterior and short. (Subphylum Hemichordata)
(Wormlike chordates) (Balanoglossus)
(Rhabdopleura)

Special Characteristics

Wormlike, soft-bodied animals with short notochord in anterior end; paired gill slits in anterior part of trunk; body usually with collar and proboscis; nervous system with dorsal and ventral tissue; circulatory system functions as invertebrate system; dioecious; marine; sometimes listed as separate phylum.

Phylum 12. Chordata; Subphylum Urochordata (u-ro-kor-da'-ta)

Adults are saclike animals; body with covering; notochord present in the larvae

(Subphylum Urochordata) (Tunicata) (sea squirts) (Ciona)

Special Characteristics

Adults may be globose, tubular, or irregular in form and covered by a tunic; some sessile, some free-living; paired gill slits in adults; larvae with posterior notochord; dorsal tubular nerve cord; brain; median eye; otolith; during retrograde metamorphosis most of characteristics are lost (including notochord, nerve cord, and associated structures except for trunk ganglion); no cranium, jaws, vertebrae, or paired appendages; hermaphroditic but self-sterile; adult species called "sea squirts"; the term "Tunicata" sometimes used as subphylum name.

Phylum 12. Chordata; Subphylum Cephalochordata

Elongated, fishlike body; notochord extending the length of the body; pharyngeal gill slits; chordate characteristics persist throughout life; no jaws or distinct head

(Subphylum Cephalochordata) (Amphioxus or *Branchiostoma*)

Special Characteristics

Marine fishlike animal; myotomes; notochord from anterior to posterior persists throughout life; dorsal tubular nerve cord; dorsal and preanal fins with fin rays; many permanent, paired pharyngeal clefts (gill slits); no distinct head; no jaws, cranium, paired appendages or vertebrae; sexes separate; excretion by nephridia.

Phylum 12. Chordata; Subphylum Agnatha; Class Cyclostomata

(si-klo-sto'-ma-ta)

Long, cylindrical, eel-like bodies; seven or more pairs of gill slits; jawless; one nasal opening; notochord persists; no paired appendages (Agnatha) (lampreys, hagfish)

Special Characteristics

Aquatic animals with long cylindrical bodies; mouth jawless and suctorial with horny, rasping teeth; one median nostril; no fins or paired appendages; smooth, scaleless skin; permanent notochord; seven or more pairs of gill pouches; two-chambered heart; cold-blooded.

Phylum 12. Chordata; Subphylum Gnathostomata; Class Chondrichthyes

One pair of visceral arches modified as jaws; two nasal openings; three pairs of semicircular canals; paired appendages; separate sexes; cartilaginous fish; placoid scales; movable jaws; ventral, anterior mouth; two-chambered heart (Chondrichthyes) (sharks, rays) (*Squalus*) (*Rai*)

Special Characteristics

Marine; cartilaginous fishes; movable jaws; fins paired; rough skin with placoid scales; persistent notochord; cartilaginous vertebrae; permanent cartilaginous skeleton; gill slits (5-7) separate clefts; no gill cover or air bladder; cold-blooded; two-chambered heart; spiral valve in intestine; sexes separate.

Phylum 12. Chordata; Subphylum Vertebrata; Class Osteichthyes
Fishlike forms with paired jaws; skeleton completely or partially of bone; usually both median and lateral fins with rays; scales dermal, cycloid, ganoid, ctenoid; gills covered by opercula; two-chambered heart (Osteichthyes) (True bony fishes)
Special Characteristics
Aquatic with jaws; paired pectoral and pelvic fins, single median fins supported by fin rays; usually dermal scales; bony skeleton; gills supported by bony or cartilaginous gill arches; operculum present; air bladder; cold-blooded; two-chambered heart; ten pairs of cranial nerves; two nasal openings; sexes separate.

Phylum 12. Chordata; Subphylum Gnathostomata; Class Amphibia (am-fib'-ia)
Smooth, solf, moist, glandular skin; skeleton of bone, respiration by gills in the larvae and lungs in the adult; three-chambered heart (Amphibia) (frogs, toads, salamanders)
Special Characteristics
Aquatic or semiaquatic; larva respiration by gills, adult by lungs; skin, mouth, jaws present; usually two pairs of legs; scaleless, moist skin; skeleton primarily of bone with two occipital condyles; two nostrils connected to buccal cavity; heart with three chambers; nucleated blood cells; ten cranial nerves; dioecious; fertilization external.

Phylum 12. Chordata; Subphylum Gnathostomata; Class Reptilia (rep-til'-i-a)
Skin usually with scales and claws throughout life; imperfect four-chambered heart; egg with embryonic membranes
(Reptilia) (turtles, snakes, lizards, crocodiles)
Special Characteristics
Terrestrial animals usually with scales, sometimes scutes; lungs as respiratory structures; jaws; usually two pairs of legs; digits with claws; 12 pairs of cranial nerves; bony skeleton; cold-blooded; imperfectly formed four-chambered heart; skull with one occipital condyle; dioecious; internal fertilization; land egg with embryonic membranes.

Phylum 12. Chordata; Subphylum Gnathostomata; Class Aves (a'-vez)

Body covered with feathers; anterior appendages modified for flight; homothermal; four-chambered heart (Aves) (birds)

Special Characteristics

Terrestrial animals covered with feathers; mouth with beak; forelimbs are wings; hindlimbs adapted for perching; skull with one occipital condyle; no teeth; warm-blooded; nucleated blood cells; dioecious; internal fertilization; one ovary; respiration by lungs; no urinary bladder; fetal membranes (amnion and chorion) as in reptiles and mammals.

Phylum 12. Chordata; Subphylum Gnathostomata; Class Mammalia (ma-ma'-li-a)

Body at least partially covered by hair; diaphragm; four chambered heart; lungs as respiratory structures; placenta (Mammalia) (dogs, man, horses, whales, monkeys, etc.)

Special Characteristics

Body at least partially covered by hair; mammary glands; many skin glands (sebaceous, scent, sweat); paired lungs; paired jaws; bony skeleton; two occipital condyles; nails, claws, or hoofs present on digits; warm-blooded; four-chambered heart (two auricles, two ventricles); well-developed brain (both cerebrum and cerebellum); muscular diaphragm; fetal membranes (amnion, chorion, allantois, placenta).

PROFESSIONAL GUIDANCE OF STUDENTS

Professional guidance for students is one of the primary areas in which the assistant may be most effective in representing the biology department. This guidance means providing information concerning available types of professional avenues and goals for a student's future work. Perhaps the majority of college students do not know definitely what their major interest for life's work will be until after their first two college years. Initial major interests change from time to time as the student grows in age and experience. The assistant is in contact with many students who are still seeking a satisfying professional goal. The assistant should therefore be broadly familiar with information regarding the biological sciences, the health sciences, and the agricultural sciences, since many of his students will have specific interests in pursuing careers in one of such professional areas.

The Occupational Outlook Handbook

The assistant should procure a personal or a departmental copy of the excellent professional guidance book, *The Occupational Outlook Handbook* compiled by the U.S. Department of Labor. It is available from the Superintendent of Documents, U.S. Government Printing Office, Washington, D.C., 20402. Price $4.75.

This comprehensive volume, including general employment information for choosing a career, discusses the economic framework and the kinds of jobs there are and will be. It considers the outlook for occupational change, and specific attention is given to concrete definitions of the various occupations. The assistant will learn where the worker will be employed, training essentials, other qualifications, and opportunities for advancement afforded by each area of work. Earnings to be expected, working conditions, and where to go and whom to write for further information regarding specific vocations are also included in the volume.

This is the type of information a professionally minded departmental assistant will find most helpful as he becomes more closely acquainted with students and seeks to aid them in mapping their futures. The assistant is often in a closer contact with students in dormitory, campus, and recreational life than is the professor. Such close contacts can open the way for rewarding discussions of guidance and future careers.

The assistant will find specific information in *The Occupational Outlook Handbook* regarding the following four specially relevant areas: (1) elementary, secondary, college, and university teaching and research; (2) health service occupations; (3) biological sciences; and (4) agricultural occupations.

Specific health service information is presented regarding (1) registered professional nurses; (2) physicians; (3) pharmacists; (4) dentists; (5) X-ray technicians; (6) medical technologists; (7) dieticians; (8) dental laboratory technicians; (9) veterinarians; (10) optometrists; (11) osteopathic physicians; (12) hospital administra-

tors; (13) dental hygienists; (14) physical therapists; (15) podia-
trists; (16) occupational therapists; and (17) medical record
librarians.

Biological sciences information is presented regarding (1) bot-
anists; (2) microbiologists; (3) agronomists; (4) anatomists; (5)
biochemists; (6) biophysicists; (7) embryologists; (8) entomolo-
gists; (9) geneticists; (10) horticulturists; (11) husbandry specialists;
(12) nutritionists; (13) pathologists; (14) pharmacologists; (15)
physiologists; and (16) phytopathologists.

Specific agricultural occupations information is presented regarding (1) agricultural extension service workers; (2) soil scientists;
(3) soil conservationists; and (4) farm service jobs.

THE LABORATORY PREPARATION FILE CARD

An effective and time-saving approach in preparing to conduct the
biology laboratory period is the preparation of individual cards which
include the names and needed quantities of all specimens and supplies to be used by a given number of students. These cards are then
filed in order of the scheduled laboratories and used by the assistant
as guides for arranging preparations for students in the laboratory in
anticipation of a particular laboratory date.

The assistant, working with the lecturer or the laboratory director,
can study the laboratory manual used and decide many days or weeks
in advance that particular items or specimens are needed. He should
then make a permanent record of such needs on the various file
cards and place his orders for supplies in sufficient advance of the day
of use that all necessities will be available.

Illustrations of the organization and content of laboratory preparation file cards should be helpful. For example, a biology laboratory
on "The Cell Principle—Animal and Plant Tissues" would call for
items in the following Illustration A to be placed by the assistant on
the laboratory preparation file card and filed for the assistant's future
reference at the proper time:

Illustration A

(1) Prepared slides on animal tissues needed: (a) Squamous epithelium slides (b) Columnar epithelium slides (c) Fibrous
connective tissue (d) Hyaline cartilage (e) Bone (f) Human

blood and frog blood (g) Striated muscle (h) Smooth muscle (i) Nerve cells.

(2) Enough slides of the above will be needed for 36 students.

(3) Individual microscopes, lamps, and drawing supplies will also be needed.

(4) Date on which this laboratory is to be conducted: Friday, April 4.

Illustration B

Title of laboratory exercise: "Properties and Activities of Protoplasm."

(1) Needed items in laboratory: (a) *Elodea* leaf (b) Gill of living clam (c) Living frog (d) Anesthetic for frog (e) Frog board (f) Living sensitive plant (*Mimosa*) (g) Clean dissecting needles (h) Matches (i) Flashlight with fresh dry cells (j) Alcohol (k) Distilled water (l) Clean pipettes (m) Suspension of carmine in water.

(2) *Elodea* and Clam in quantities sufficient for 23 students.

(3) Frog and frog board work to be done as demonstrations by assistant.

(4) Distilled water, carmine, alcohol, and matches to be secured from stock room.

(5) Orders must be placed for *Elodea* and Clam not later than January 3, so that they will arrive by January 17.

(6) This laboratory will be conducted on January 18.

The assistant may use the foregoing two illustrations to set up any number of laboratory preparation file cards. Such cards assure that needed details are worked out in advance, that supplies are ordered, that any required conferences with professors are held in advance, and that sufficient time and attention are given to the specific laboratory period to make it an effective learning experience for the students.

PLANNING AND CONDUCTING THE LABORATORY PRACTICAL EXAMINATION

The practical examination consists of permitting the student to observe again some specimen, preparation, or organ with which he has worked before and to recall certain structural or functional information about it under a time limitation. The practical examination is generally a very formal testing experience. The examination includes a set number of observations for the students, who rotate in turn for viewing while marking their answers in numbered columns down the examination page. Answers generally consist of short one- or two-word responses. The time limitation may vary from 30 seconds to one minute for each observation.

Practicals may be classified into three major types: (1) the Group Practical which consists of total class observation of preparations at a number of stations set up on laboratory tables for answer responses by the students, who rotate from station to station according to a verbal time signal given by the assistant; (2) Individual Recall of specific structures in such a specimen as the shark while the professor or assistant points out the structures personally to the student; (3) Projected Structures which students recognize from projections thrown onto a screen while the professor or assistant points out the specifics of the examination.

The Group Practical is generally set up by the assistant, who obtains approval of his completed set-up from the professor before the practical is actually given to the student. It is generally advisable to secure the help of at least one other assistant in the laboratory for the time during which the examination is given. One assistant should watch the time and call the signal to move to the various stations. The other assistant should observe the general movement of students and watch the specimens so that no specimen or structure is touched as students move from place to place; he should also be available for handling any general problem that may arise during the timed quiz.

The practical should be limited to a total of not more than 25 students at any single quizzing session. If there are more than 25 students (say 75 or 100 who are enrolled in the regular laboratories) the total group of students should be broken down into small groups of 25 and a series of tests administered at different times, with groups reporting for the practical only at their scheduled times.

Special Pointers in Planning and Executing the Practical Examination

The following special pointers should be adhered to as the assistant plans, sets up, and executes the Group Practical:

(1) Discuss with the lecturing professor or the laboratory director just what that person desires with regard to the specific questions and specimens to be included on the examination.

(2) Divide the number of questions equally among the number of specimens that have been studied. For example, if frog, shark, and pig have been studied, a 100-question practical would include about 33 questions based on each specimen.

(3) The wording of the practical examination question is a critical factor in the student's interpretation and choice of answers. The assistant should give careful attention to wording his questions clearly so that there is no frustration in the mind of the student regarding what is expected of him in responding to the question.

(4) The assistant should prepare himself a tray of materials to be used for setting up the stations for the practical. This tray should include (a) index cards upon which questions are to be written; (b) pen and ink for writing the questions (a typewriter may be used); (c) forceps for clearing and lifting structures as questions are developed and written on the index cards; (d) straight pins for sticking into or through desired specimen structures; (e) colored twine for running from the pinned structure to the index card with its question; (f) scissors for cutting parts of the specimen or for cutting the twine and index cards; and (g) Scotch tape for anchoring questions and twine.

(5) Make sure that each specimen used at each station is carefully dissected and that all organs are cleared for easy viewing when the student arrives at the station with its specimen and its question. Wide regions of each specimen should be completely visible so that all relationships or organs are easily seen. Remember that the student is observing, thinking, and recalling under pressure, so he must be given every consideration regarding the quality of the dissections on which his observations and answers must be based.

(6) In setting up the practical, it may be advisable to use new, fresh specimens that have been specially dissected rather than old specimens which students themselves have dissected. When fresh dissections are desired, the assistant and his co-workers are required to do the actual dissections of the fresh specimens in preparation for the practical.

(7) Specimens in bottles should be clearly and readily observable. Microscopic preparations should be properly placed on the stage and well-lighted. Any projected slides or structures for questions should be clearly seen by each student as the question is developed from the projection by the assistant.

(8) To assure that the questions, index cards, twine position, microscope preparations, and the specimen parts have not been moved during the mechanics of taking the practical, the assistant should carefully check the condition of the specimens or preparations against his list of questions and answers immediately before admitting the students for the practical and immediately afterward. If anything has been inadvertently moved or disturbed during the actual quiz time, so that the specimen is adversely affected, the assistant should delete the related question from consideration in grading.

(9) In preparing the student for taking the practical, the assistant should demonstrate the numbering arrangement of stations and the importance of the time limitation. He should caution the student against touching the specimens, twine, and question cards. He should demonstrate specifically how the students will move from one numbered question to another, in order, when the signal "move" is called. He should tell the students how and where to surrender their papers when the examination has been completed.

(10) The assistant should remind the groups of the importance of honesty and independence while taking the practical, emphasizing that no dishonesty will be tolerated.

(11) Once a student has passed a certain station after his time limit, he must not be permitted to return to that station later during the practical.

(12) Immediately after administering the practical examination, the assistant must see that the laboratory is completely cleared of students, specimens are returned to preservatives and cabinets, and preparations at each station are removed so that normal laboratory routine can be re-established.

(13) The assistant should arrange his personal schedule so that he provides himself ample time for grading the practicals, recording these grades in his own record book, and for turning in the grade of each student to the professor in charge of the course.

THE ROLE OF THE ASSISTANT IN FIELD TRIP ACTIVITIES

Field trips for various purposes will be called for at different times by the department head or instructional staff. These trips may be conducted for the purpose of studying the ecology of plants or animals in a natural setting or for learning the organization and operation of some community facility such as a health department laboratory. There are certain general principles that apply to all field trips, and the assistant must become thoroughly familiar with these.

Sites and Environmental Factors in Plant and Animal Study in the Field

For field trips to selected areas for ecological observations and good collections, a successful field trip conductor must know at least a few of the fundamentals of plant and animal distribution. He must be aware of such environmental factors as (1) water supply (2) light (3) temperature (4) oxygen supply (5) hydogen ion concentration and (6) fertility of the soil. These factors determine the types of plant communities to be found and, consequently, the types of animal forms likely to be encountered. A general review of ecological factors from selected texts will serve as a good preparation activity for the assistant. He should also become thoroughly acquainted with the nature of the area before he takes students to it for study. He should know that certain forms are found only about ponds, swamps, or bogs, and that many species found in a beech-maple forest are not found in oak-hickory association, swamp forests, or grasslands.

The assistant can learn from conversations with the older inhabitants of a community many interesting facts concerning vegetation changes that have occurred in the region through the years.

The assistant should work with the department head or permanent teaching staff to locate suitable agricultural lands, pastured grasslands, wood lots, ponds, and streams that promise interesting field studies. Quite a variety of species can be located, collected, listed, and classified from these localities. A study of weeds, insects, rodents, birds, fur-bearing animals, game, cultivated and native trees, shrubs, and plant and animal diseases of an agricultural region will greatly stimulate student interest in biology. The assistant must realize that an available jungle of native vegetation is not necessarily a prerequisite to successful field trips.

Student Responsibilities in the Field

Each student should be required to take notes in the field. The assistant should encourage the students to:
(1) Take all notes on the spot;
(2) Take complete notes;

(3) Check observations at the end of the trip (the assistant should provide time for such checking);

(4) Make accurate drawings;

(5) Learn to observe carefully and accurately.

Field Equipment

(1) Field glasses,

(2) Hand lenses,

(3) Cameras,

(4) Maps (geographic survey maps are available for much of the country from Geological Survey, Washington 25, D.C.),

(5) Glassware, plastic bags, and strainers,

(6) Formalin and alcohol,

(7) Cages,

(8) Nets and seines,

(9) Paper folds for insects such as butterflies,

(10) Killing bottles,

(11) Collection boxes.

Field Studies Other than Plant and Animal Sites

Field trips other than those for studying animal and plant sites include those to:

(1) Packing houses to study smoking, salting, drying, canning, and refrigeration,

(2) Pasteurizing plants to study methods of pasteurizing,

(3) Canneries,

(4) Health laboratories,

(5) Vaccine and serum laboratories,

(6) Tanneries,

(7) Water supply systems,

(8) Sewage disposal plants,

(9) Cheese factories,

(10) Hospitals,

(11) Veterinary clinics.

The Specific Role of the Assistant in Field Trip Activities

Special pointers regarding the assistant's role in field trip activities may be summarized. He should (1) determine specific field trip objectives centered around the quarter's or semester's course work; (2) make necessary contacts early; (3) secure a list of possibilities for exploration in the locality and decide with the department head or instructional personnel on the most important places to study, since time is usually limited; (4) plan with the class and contact the host about the specific types of help and guidance needed when the assistant arrives with the group; (5) during the field trip, allow the guide to do the talking, discourage inattention and casual talk among students, but encourage questions from them; (6) follow up the field trip with (a) films, (b) student reports, (c) individual and group research on various phases of the trip, (d) readings or further reference work on the subject or specimens studied, (e) observation and classification of specimens collected, and (f) preparation of the better specimens for purposes of permanent display.

THE ASSISTANT AND THE PROFESSIONAL VOCABULARY

A criterion for designating mastery of a subject is the ease with which one handles its vocabulary. To a very large degree, biological science emphasizes a specialized vocabulary or terminology, and the student is frequently required to master pronunciations and meanings of terms and expressions. Classically, the biological word may be traced to its Greek or Latin root. Terms that are used in the modern text or laboratory situation can be broken into segments that illustrate the Greek or Latin.

The following selection of terms and their original roots will be helpful to the assistant as he works with students to derive and interpret the meaning of various terms encountered during course experiences. This list is relatively short; it serves only to introduce the importance and the prevalence of the Greek and Latin influences in the assistant's experience and to encourage him to develop increasing familiarity with such roots from the variety of texts and glossaries available to him.

Biological Terms

abdomen, L; *abdomen*, belly.

abducens, L; *abducere*, to draw away from.

absorption, L; *a*, from; *sorbere*, to suck up.

adenoid, G; *aden*, gland; *eidos*, shape.

adipose, L; *adeps*, fat.

anatomy, G; *ana*, up; *tome*, cutting.

antiseptic, G; *anti*, against; *sepsis*, putrefaction.

antitoxin, G; *anti*, against; *toxikon*, poison for arrows.

aorta, G; *aorte*, to lift.

appendicitis, L; *ad*, to; *pendere*, to hang.

atrial, L; *atrium*, a central room.

atrophy, G; a, without; trephein, to nourish.

auricle, L; auricula, a little ear.

autotrophic, G; autos, self; trephein, to nourish.

axon, G; axon, axle.

biceps, L; bi, two; caput, head.

bicuspid, L; bis, twice; cuspis, point.

biology, G; bios, life; logos, discourse.

bisexual, L; bis, two; sexus, sex.

blastocoele, G; blastos, germ; koilos, hollow.

blastocyst, G; blastos; kystis, bladder.

brachiopoda, G; brachium, arm; pous, foot.

brachium, L; brachium, arm.

branchia, G; branchia, gills.

bronchia, G; bronchos, windpipe.

buccal, L; bucca, cheek or mouth.

bursaria, L; bursa, pouch.

caecum, L; caecus, blind.

canaliculi, L; canaliculus, a small channel.

cardiac, G; kardia, heart.

cerebellum, L; cerebrum, brain.

cervical, L; cervix, neck.

chiasma, G; chiasma, crossmark.

coccus, G; kokkos, a seed.

colon, G; kolon, member.

costa, G; costa, a rib.

cranium, G; kranion, head.

cricoid, G; krikos, a ring; eidos, form.

cusp, L; cuspis, a point.

cutaneous, L; cutis, skin.

cyst, G; kystis, a bladder.

deltoid, G; delta, fourth letter of the Greek alphabet, triangular in form.

dendrites, G; dendron, tree.

dentine, L; dens, tooth.

depressor, L; deprimere, to lower.

dermis, G; derma, skin.

diaphragm, G; dia, between; phragnyme, to enclose.

diffusion, L; dis, apart; fundere, to pour.

digit, L; digitus, finger.

dilator, L; dilitare, to expand.

distal, L; dis, apart; stare, to stand.

ectoblast, G; ektos, without; blastos, bud.

ectoplasm, G; ektos, outside; plasma, something moulded.

ectoblast, G; ektos, without; blastos, something moulded.

egestion, L; ex, out; gerere, to carry.

endocardium, G; endon, within; kardia, heart.

endoderm, G; endon, within; derma, skin.

epicardium, G; epi, upon; kardia, heart.

epicranium, G; epi, upon; kranion, skull.

epididymis, G; epi, upon; didvmos, testicle.

epinephrin, G; epi, upon; nephros, kidney.

episternum, G; epi, upon; sternum, breast bone.

epithelium, G; epi, upon; thele, nipple.

erythrocytes, G; erythros, red; kytos, hollow.

ethmoid, G; ethmos, seive; eidos, shape.

excretion, L; ex, out; cernere, to shift.

expiration, L; ex, out; spirare, to breathe.

facial, L; facies, face.

falciform, L; falx, sickle.

fascia, L; fascia, a hand or bandage.

femur, L; thigh.

filiform, L; filum, thread; forma, form.

fissure, L; fissus, cleft.

flexion, L; flexus, bent.

follicle, L; folliculus, a little bag.

fornix, L; fornix, an arch or vault.

fossa, L; fossa, a pit or cavity.

frenulum, L; frenulum, a bridle or bit.

frontal, L; frons, brow.

fundus, L; fundus, the bottom; the base of an organ.

fungiform, L; *fungus*, a mushroom.
ganglia, G; *ganglion*, little tumor.
gastric, G; *gaster*, stomach.
gastrocnemius, G; *gaster*, stomach; *kneme*, shank.
gastrovascular cavity, G; *gaster*, stomach; L; *vasculum*, a small vessel.
gene, G; *gene*, descent.
germ, L; *germen*, bud.
glomerulus, L; *glomus*, a ball of yarn.
glossopharyngeal, G; *glossa*, tongue; *pharynx*, pharynx.
glottis, G; *glotta*, tongue.
gluteus, G; *gloutos*, rump.
gyrus, G; *gyros*, round.
haploid, G; *haploos*, simple; *eiodos*, like.
hemiazygous vein, G; *hemi*, half; *azygos*, unyoked.
hepatic, L; *hepar*, liver.
heterotrophic, G; *heteros*, other; *trephein*, to nourish.
hormone, G; *hormao*, to excite.
humerus, L; *humerus*, the bone of the upper arm.
hyaline, G; *hyalos*, glass.
hymenium, G; *hymen*, skin.
hyoid, G; *hyoeides*, Y-shaped.
hypertrophy, G; *hyper*, above; *trophe*, nourishment.
hypodermis, G; *hypo*, under; *derma*, skin.
hypogastric, G; *gaster*, belly.
hypoglossal, G; *glossa*, tongue.
hypo-ischium, G; *ischion*, hip.
hypopharynx, G; *pharynx*, gullet.
hypothalamus, G; *thalamos*, chamber.
ileum, G; *eilo*, twist.
iliopsoas, L; *ilium*, the flank; G; *psoa*, a muscle of the loins.
impregnation, L; *impraegnare*, to fertilize.
incisor, L; *incido*, cut into.
indentation, L; *indentare*, to indent.
ingestion, L; *ingestus*, taken in.

innominate, L; *innominatus*, without a name.
internode, L; *nodus*, knot.
interosseous, L; *os*, bone.
intestine, L; *intestinus*, inside.
invaginate, L; *in*, into; *vagina*, sheath.
irritability, L; *irritare*, to provoke.
ischium, G; *ischion*, hip.
isthmus, G; *isthmos*, neck.
jugular, L; *jugulum*, the collar bone.
lacunae, L; *lacunna*, cavity.
larynx, G; *larynx*, gullet.
lateral, L; *latus*, side.
leucocyte, G; *leukos*, white; *kytos*, hollow.
ligament, L; *ligamentum*, bandage.
linea alba, L; *linea*, line; *alba*, white.
lingula, L; *lingula*, little tongue.
lymph, L; *lymphia*, clear water.
mandible, L; *mandibula*, jaw.
masseter, G; *maseter*, a chew.
mastoid, G; *mastos*, breast.
matrix, L; *mater*, mother.
maxilla, L; *maxilla*, the jaw bone.
media, L; *medius*, middle.
mediastinum, L; *mediastinum*, servant.
medullary, L; *medulla*, marrow, pith.
mesentery, G; *mesos*, middle; *enteron*, gut.
mesocolon, G; *mesos*, middle; *kolon*, large intestine.
mesoderm, G; *mesos*, middle; *derma*, skin.
metatarsus, G; *meta*, L; *tarsus*, ankle.
minimum, L; *minimus*, least.
mucosa, L; *mucus*, mucus.
myocardium, G; *mys*, muscle; *kardia*, heart.
nasal, L; *nasus*, nose.
nephridium, G; *nephros*, kidney.
node, L; *nodus*, knob.
obturator, L; *obturare*, to stop up.
occiput, L; *occiput*, the back of the head; *ob*, over against; *caput*, head.

oculomotor, L; *oculus*, eye; *moveo*, to move.

olfactory, L; *olere*, smell.

omentum, L; *omentum*, a fold.

opaque, L; *opacus*, darkened.

operculum, G; *operculum*, a lid.

ophthalmic, G; *opthalmikos*, of or for the eye.

organ, L; *organum*, an implement.

ossification, L; *os fio*, to become.

osteoblasts, G; *osteon*, bone; *blastos*, a bud.

oviducts, L; *ovum*, egg; *duco*, to lead.

palate, L; *palatum*, palate.

palpus, L; *palpare*, to feel.

pancreas, G; *pan*, all; *kreas*, flesh.

parietal, L; *paries*, wall.

parotid, G; *para*, beside; *ous*, ear.

pectoral, L; *pectoralis*, referring to the chest.

pelvis, L; *pelvis*, basin, the pelvis.

periderm, G; *peri*, around; *derma*, skin.

peridural, G; *peri*, around; L; *dura*, hard.

peritoneal, G; *peri*, around; *teino*, stretch.

plexus, L; *plexus*, interweaving.

podium, G; *pous*, foot.

pubis, L; *pubes*, mature.

pyloris, G; *pyloros*, a gatekeeper.

pyramids, L; *pyramis*, a pyramid.

rectum, L; *rectus*, straight.

reproduction, L; *re pro*, forth; *ducere*, to lead.

rugae, L; *ruga*, a wrinkle.

sacral, L; *sacer*, sacred.

semitendinosus, L; *simi*, half; *tendere*, to stretch.

sclere, G; *skleros*, hard.

septa, L; *septum*, partition.

sphenoid, G; *sphen*, wedge.

sternal, G; *sternon*, breast.

sternohyoid, G; *sternon hyoides*, Y-shaped.

stomach, G; *stomachos*, throat, gullet.

striated, L; *stria*, a channel.

subarachnoid, L; *sub*, under; G; *arachne*, spider, *eidos*, resemblance.

subdural, L; *sub*, under; *durus*, hard.

sublingua, L; *sub*, under; *lingua*, tongue.

submucosa, L; *sub*, under; *mucosus*, mucus.

sulci, L; *sulcus*, furrow.

temporal, L; *tempus*, temple.

tendon, L; *tensus*, stretch.

tensor, L; *tensus*, stretch.

thoracic, L; *thorax*, thorax.

thymus, G; *thymon*, thyme.

thyroid, G; *thyreos*, shield.

tibia, L; *tibia*, the shin bone.

tissue, G; *tissu*, woven.

tonsil, L; *tonsilla*, tonsil.

toxic, G; *toxikon*, poison.

trapezius, G; *trapeza*, table.

triceps, L; *tres*, three; *caput*, head.

tricuspid valves, L; *tres*, three; *cuspis*, point.

tubercle, L; *tuberculum*, a small hump.

ulna, L; *ulna*, elbow.

ureter, G; *ouron*, urine.

uterus, L; *uterus*, womb.

valve, L; *valva*, fold.

vas deferens, L; *vas deferre*, to carry from.

ventricle, L; *venter*, belly.

vertebrata, L; *vertebra*, joint.

vesicles, L; *vesicula*, a vesicle.

vestibule, L; *vestibulum*, a passage.

villi, L; *villus*, shaggy hair.

viscera, L; *viscus*, internal organ.

xiphisternum, G; *xiphos*, sword; L; *sternum*, breast.

xiphoid, G; *xiphos*, sword; *eidos*, shape.

zygomatic, G; *zygoma*, yoke.

COMPREHENSIVE AIDS TO DEVELOPMENT OF
BIOLOGICAL TECHNIQUES AND METHODS

For many years the General Biological Supply House, a reliable and progressive firm, has supplied to biology departmental personnel a series of extremely helpful publications called "Turtox Service Leaflets." These leaflets deal with a wide variety of laboratory and teaching techniques and methods. They are comprehensive, well-organized, and clear. They provide a wealth of ideas, suggestions, and precautions regarding numerous practical activities.

The assistant should secure this entire series of leaflets and seek to master their contents by regular study. The complete series of numbered titles is listed below, with their topics and subtopics, to illustrate their nature and value. The assistant may use this listing as a convenient index to the specific information supplied by any particular leaflet as he has need of its use in the departmental program.

The assistant should request the leaflets by writing on departmental letterhead to the General Biological Supply House, 8200 South Hoyne Avenue, Chicago 20, Illinois. Supplies may be limited. The leaflets may be obtained free under certain conditions, or there may be a nominal cost.

Turtox Service Leaflets

Number 1—*How To Make An Insect Collection*
Field trips; collecting equipment; mounting equipment; directions for mounting; labeling; method of relaxing and pinning dried Lepidoptera; care of the collection.

Number 2—*Preserving Zoological Specimens*
Narcotization; fixatives; fixation; preservation.

Number 3—*Preserving Botanical Specimens*
Preserving specimens for laboratory study; preserving specimens for microscopic examination; preserving specimens for display purposes; other methods.

Number 4—*The Care of Protozoan Cultures in the Laboratory*
Care of cultures; *Amoeba*; *Chaos Chaos*; *Paramecium*; pure-line cultures of *Paramecium* for general study and demonstration of conjugation; *Euglena*; *Stentor*; the

culture of other protozoa sometimes studied; culture of coelenterates.

Number 5—*Starting and Maintaining a Fresh-Water Aquarium*
How to start; feeding the aquarium animals

Number 6—*Growing Fresh-Water Algae in the Laboratory*
Blue-green algae; green algae.

Number 7—*The Care of Frogs and Other Amphibians*
Frogs; tree frogs; frog eggs; toads; salamanders.

Number 8—*How to Prepare Microscope Slides of Simple Objects*
Mounting specimens in medium; whole mounts; teased preparations; freehand sections.

Number 9—*How to Make Skeletons*
The preparation of dry ligamentous skeletons; preparing disarticulated skeletons; semicartilaginous skeletons; the preparation of cartilaginous skeletons.

Number 10—*The School Terrarium*
The desert terrarium; the woodland terrarium; the bog terrarium; the semiaquatic terrarium; notes on terrarium care.

Number 11—*Plants for the Fresh-Water Aquarium*
Rooted plants; terminal growing plants; floating plants.

Number 12—*Demonstration and Display Materials*
Dry specimens; liquid specimens; the care of demonstration specimens.

Number 13—*Rearing the Silkworm Moth*
General information; schedule of developing time.

Number 14—*A Selected List of Books for the Biology Library*
Author, title, publisher, price; biology; botany; zoology; comparative anatomy; entomology; embryology; ornithology; nature study; microbiology-parasitology; microscope slide technique; general science; miscellaneous.

Number 15—*The Culture of Drosophila Flies and Their Use in Demonstrating Mendel's Law of Heredity*
Media; containers; sterilization; storage of cultures; avoiding contamination of cultures; distinguishing males from females; securing virgin flies; technique of examining the flies; mating the flies; some suggested matings.

Number 16—*The Culture of Planaria and Its Use in Regeneration Experiments*
General laboratory study; regeneration experiments.

Number 17—*Incubation, Fixation, and Mounting of Chick Embryos*
Incubation; removing the embryo; fixation; whole
months; sections.
Number 18—*Insectivorous Plants*
Pitcher-plants; sundews Venus Flytrap; bladderwort;
butterwort; cultivation; seed culture.
Number 19—*Special Projects for Biology Students*
General projects; field projects; living material projects;
projects for the laboratory; monthly projects.
Number 20—*Notes on Marine Aquaria*
Collecting and shipping; the aquarium tank; sand; sea
water; maintaining the right concentration; temperature
of the water; aeration of the water; light; the animals;
feeding the animals; temporary marine aquaria;
summary.
Number 21—*Preparation, Injection, and Care of Embalmed Specimens*
Embalming equipment; preparing the animal for embalming; the embalming process; injecting the circulatory system; the care of embalmed specimens.
Number 22—*How to Make Laboratory Drawings*
Preliminary study; materials; size of drawings; laying
out the drawing; shading; labeling; neatness.
Number 23—*Feeding Aquarium and Terrarium Animals*
Snails; fishes, native species; fishes, warm-water species
(tropicals); salamanders; toads; frogs; tree frogs; alli-
gators; lizards; snakes; turtles; rats and mice; guinea pigs.
Number 24—*Preparing and Caring for a Herbarium Collection*
Equipment; collecting specimens; pressing the speci-
mens; mounting specimens; arranging and storing the
collection.
Number 25—*Non-Flowering Plants*
Lichens; bryophytes; pteridophytes.
Number 26—*Making Biology Charts*
Materials; drawings; mounting.
Number 27—*Brine Shrimp and Other Crustaceans*
Brine shrimp; glass shrimp; fairy shrimp; *Daphnia;* other
fresh-water crustaceans; crayfish.
Number 28—*Reptiles in the School Laboratory*
Alligators; lizards; turtles; snakes; poisonous species.

Number 29—*Blood Typing*
Classification of blood groups; the three systems of nomenclature for blood groups; antigen-antibody reaction; medico-legal tests; blood typing methods.

Number 30—*Growing Plants in Nutrient Culture Media*
Preparing the medium; planting; technique.

Number 31—*Micro-replicas*

Number 32—*The Culture and Microscopy of Molds*
Collecting molds; media preparation; transfer method; microscopic observation; supplementary instructions.

Number 33—*Embedding Specimens in Improved and Easy-to-Use Transparent Plastic*
Simplified room-temperature embedments; treatment of specimens prior to embedment.

Number 34—*The Care of Living Insects in the School Laboratory*
Tenebrio-mealworms; butterfly chrysalids; praying mantis; walking-stick; grasshoppers; aquatic insects; roaches; termites.

Number 35—*Studying Ants in Observation Nests*
The observation nest; collecting the ants; starting the colony; care of the colony—water and food; general nest observation; recognition of nestmates; mixed colony observation; effects of temperature; special behavior; parasites, etc; individual behavior; foraging; the purchased ant colony.

Number 36—*Practical Microscopy*
Illumination; eye care; illuminating the 16mm. objective; the 4mm. objective; illuminating the homogeneous oil immersion objective; adjusting the research lamp and establishing Koehler illumination; numerical aperture; resolving power; care of the microscope.

Number 37—*Flowering Plants in the Laboratory*
Bulbs and tubers; seeds; ginkgo seeds; lotus seeds; greenhouse plants; orchids and airplants; wild flowers; plants to demonstrate vegetative reproduction.

Number 38—*Moth Cocoons*
General information; care of the cocoons.

Number 39—*The Fresh-Water Hydras*
Form and appearance; occurrence; where to collect; how

to care for hydra in the laboratory; feeding; reproduction; depression; notes on culturing *Daphnia*.

Number 40—*The Care of Rats, Mice, Hamsters, and Guinea Pigs*

Number 41—*Collection and Culture of Earthworms and Other Annelids*
Lumbricus terrestris; collection; cultures of enchytrae worms; aquatic earthworms; leeches.

Number 42—*Laboratory Dissections*
Prerequisites of a good dissection; dissecting the specimen; orderliness and cleanliness.

Number 43—*Embryology in the High School Biology Course*
Starfish; Ascaris; wild fruitfly; *Drosophila*; frog; chick.

Number 44—*Growing Fern Prothallia in the Laboratory*
Germinating spores; growing prothallia; liquid medium; flower pot culture of prothallia; Costello method; agar method; notes on mature fern culture.

Number 45—*Lantern Slides Any Teacher Can Make*
The plain glass slide; the gelatine slide; the ground glass slide; on cellophane; photographic slides; other methods.

Number 46—*The Study of Fossil Specimens*
Fossil animals; fossil plants.

Number 47—*Plant Experiments with Gibberellic Acid*
To make up solutions; indoor or outdoor; methods of application; seed treatment; using controls; general effects on vegetative growth; plants responsive to powder solution; vast experimental possibilities.

Number 48—*Aquarium Troubles: Their Prevention and Remedies*

Number 49—*Nutrition Experiments*
General remarks; the care of white rats; laboratory experiments.

Number 50—*Elementary Experiments in Bacteriology*
General remarks; simple experiments; techniques required in introductory bacteriology; more complex experiments.

Number 51—*Hydroponics: Growing Plants in Nutrient and in Deficient Nutrient Solutions Without Soil*
Laboratory water culture outfit; individual culture outfit; deficient nutrient solutions; deficient plant growth chemical sets; sufficient plant growth chemical sets; composition of individual chemical units.

Number 52—*Advanced Experiments in Bacteriology*
> Techniques required in advanced bacteriology; transfers; supplementary instructions for bacteriology sets for the cultural differentiation of pure Gram negative pathogens; supplementary instructions for securing specific cultural characteristics; supplementary instructions for opening hermetically sealed anaerobic culture tubes.

Number 53—*Experiments in Radiobiology*
> Germination and growth studies in irradiated seeds; methods of irradiation; materials needed; experimental procedure; evaluation of experimental findings; second-generation studies.

Number 54—*Plant and Animal Hormone Experiments*
> Facilities; precautions; root-forming experiments; vitamin B; experiments; colchicine experiments; experimental suggestions; seedlings; buds.

Number 55—*The Injection of Laboratory Specimens*
> Invertebrates; vertebrates: the frog, *Necturus*, turtle, pigeon, cat.

Number 56—*Simplified Microphotography*
> General remarks; camera with lens; duplicate cameras without lenses; advanced methods; the star test; working with an exposure meter.

Number 57—*The Organization and Activities of a Biology Club*
> Formal organization; general suggestions.

Number 58—*Basic Floor Plans for the High School Biology Department*
> Floor location; exposure; use of light; room darkening; water; gas; electricity; floors, walls, and ceilings.

Number 59—*Basic Laboratory Equipment for the High School Biology Course*
> Quantity, catalog number, material, and lot price given for microscope slides; museum preparations; skeletons; models, charts and quiz sheets; Kodachrome lantern slides; apparatus; glassware; plastic; chemicals; NDEA.

Number 60—*Plant Culture with Artificial Light*
> Quality of light; small growth chambers; quantity of light; rooting of cuttings; seed germination; large growth chambers; basement culture.

STANDARD TEXTS AND REFERENCES

The assistant should strive continually to improve himself professionally and to grow in proficiency in conducting his departmental duties. Acquaintance with professional publications of various types, as well as mastery of or familiarity with a number of standard references and texts, are essential parts of the assistant's challenge to grow with his experiences.

The following selected list of books is recommended to the assistant as good investments of his time and funds, should he desire to build or increase his personal store of professional books. Many of these books will be found in his general college or departmental library. Some may be found in local book or magazine outlets, bookstores, or second-hand shops.

New publications are being produced constantly, so the following samples are intended primarily as clues that will lead to others by the same author or other authors. The assistant's acquaintance with the content and the quality of his readings from the following books may well serve to justify his recommendations for additions to the departmental or institutional library. Certainly the assistant's continual reading of such books as those listed will add tremendously to his biological knowledge and to his functional proficiency.

Recommended General Bibliography

Allen, Glover M., *Bats*, Dover T984, 1962, 368 pp., $2.00.
Asimov, Isaac, *The Bloodstream: River of Life*, Collier AS8, 1961, 221 pp., $.95.
Asimov, Isaac, *The Chemicals of Life*, Abelard-Schuman, 1954, 159 pp., $2.75.
Asimov, Isaac, *The Genetic Code*, Signet Science P2250, 1963, 187 pp., $.60.
Asimov, Isaac, *The Wellsprings of Life*, Signet Science P2066, 1960, 200 pp., $.60.
Barnett, Antony, *The Human Species*, Pelican A341, 1961, 354 pp., $1.85.
Bates, Marston, *Man in Nature*, Prentice-Hall, 1961, 116 pp., $1.75.
Bates, Marston, *The Forest and the Sea*, Mentor MD316, 1960, 216 pp., $.50.

Beck, William S., *Modern Science and the Nature of Life*, Anchor N8, 1961, 334 pp., $1.45.

Beeler, Nelson F., and Franklyn M. Branley, *Experiments with a Microscope*, Crowell, 1957, 154 pp., $2.75.

Bernard, Claude, *An Introduction to the Study of Experimental Medicine*, Dover T400, 1957, 226 pp., $1.50.

Berrill, N. J., *The Living Tide*, Premier, 1956, $.35.

Bold, Harold C., *The Plant Kingdom*, Prentice-Hall, 1960, 114 pp., $1.75.

Brandwein, Paul F., *The Gifted Student as Future Scientist*, Harcourt, 1955, 107 pp., $2.00.

Brock, Thomas (ed.), *Milestones in Microbiology*, Prentice-Hall, 1961, 275 pp., $3.95.

Buchsbaum Ralph M., *Animals Without Backbones*, Rev. ed., University of Chicago, 1948, 405 pp., $8.00.

Buchsbaum, Ralph M., *Basic Ecology*, Boxwood Press, 1957, 192 pp., $3.50.

Callison, Charles H., (ed.), *America's Natural Resources*, Ronald, 1957, 211 pp., $3.75.

Carson, Rachel L., *The Edge of the Sea*, New American Library, 1959, $.50.

Carson, Rachel L., *The Sea Around Us*, Oxford, 1951, 230 pp., $4.00; New American Library, 1954, $.35.

Cheesman, Evelyn, *Insects: Their Secret World*, Apollo A15, 1961, 246 pp., $1.75.

Christensen, Clyde, *The Molds and Man*, University of Minnesota, 1951, 244 pp., $4.00.

Clausen, Lucy W., *Insect Fact and Folklore*, Collier AS78, 1962, 222 pp., $.95.

Clendening, Logan (ed.), *Source Book of Medical History*, Dover T621, 1960, 685 pp., $2.75.

Cohen, Bernard I., *Science, Servant of Man*, Little, Brown, 1948, 362 pp., $5.00.

Cook, Gordon J., *Virus in the Cell*, Dial, 1957, $3.00.

Cousteau, J. Y., *The Silent World*, Harper, 1953, $4.75.

Cruickshank, Allan and Helen, *1001 Questions and Answers About Birds*, Dodd, Mead, 1958, $2.95.

Curtis, Brian, *The Life Story of the Fish*, Dover T929, 1949, 284 pp., $1.50.

Dampier, William C., *A Shorter History of Science*, Meridian, 1957, 190 pp., $1.25.

Dawson, E. Yale, *How to Know the Seaweeds*, Brown, 1956, 197 pp., $2.75.

Decoursey, Russell M., *The Human Organism*, McGraw-Hill, 1955, 550 pp., $6.50.

Dobzhansky, Theodosius, *Evolution, Genetics and Man*, Wiley, 1955, 398 pp., $5.50.

Dowdeswell, W. H., *Animal Ecology*, Torchbooks TB543, 1961, 209 pp., $1.50.

Dubos, Rene, *Pasteur and Modern Science*, Anchor S15, 1960, 159 pp., $.95.

Dudley, Ruth H., *Our American Trees*, Crowell, 1956, $2.75.

Fabre, Jean H., *Insect Adventure*, Dodd, 1950, 287 pp., $3.00.

Fenton, Carroll Lane, and Dorothy C. Pallas, *Trees and Their World*, Day, 1957, $3.25.

Fox, Ruth, *Great Men of Medicine*, Random, 1947, 240 pp., $3.50.

Frohse, Franz, *et al*, *Atlas of Human Anatomy* (6th ed.), Barnes and Noble 70, 1961, 180 pp., $2.95.

Fuller, Harry J., *General Botany*, College Outline 33, 1955, 196 pp., $1.25.

Gabriel, Mordecai L., and Seymour Fogel, *Great Experiments in Biology*, Prentice-Hall, 1955, 317 pp., $3.95.

Galston, Arthur W., *The Life of the Green Plant*, Prentice-Hall, 1961, 116 pp., $1.75.

Gerard, R. W., *Unresting Cells*, Torchbooks TB541, 1961, 434 pp., $2.25.

Giusti, George, and Rudolph Hoffman, *Heart: Anatomy, Function and Diseases*, Dell VY4, 1962, 120 pp., $.95.

Goldstein, Philip, *Genetics Are Easy*, Rev. Ed., Lantern Press, 1955, 338 pp., $4.00.

Goldstein, Philip, *How to do an Experiment*, Harcourt, 1957, 192 pp., $2.60.

Grant, Madeleine, *Microbiology and Human Progress*, Rinehart, 1952, 718 pp., $7.50.

Graves, Arthur Harmound, *Illustrated Guide to Trees and Shrubs*, Harper, 1956, $6.00.

Harrison, Kenneth, *A Guidebook to Biochemistry*, Cambridge, 1959, 150 pp., $1.95.

Haskins, Caryl P., *Of Societies and Men*, Compass C59, 1960, 282 pp., $1.45.

Hegner, Robert, *Parade of the Animal Kingdom*, MacMillan, 1955, 675 pp., $6.95.

Hemming, James, *Mankind Against the Killers*, Longmans, Green, 1956, $3.50.

Hoffman, Joseph G., *The Life and Death of Cells*, Doubleday, 1957, $4.50.

Hooten, Earnest A., *Up from the Ape*, Rev. ed., MacMillan, 1946, 788 pp., $7.25.

Hutchins, Ross E., *Strange Plants and Their Ways*, Rand McNally, 1958, $2.95.

Hylander, Clarence J., *The World of Plant Life*, 2d ed., MacMillan, 1956, 653 pp., $10.95.

Irvine, William, *Apes, Angels and Victorians*, McGraw-Hill, 1955, 399 pp., $5.00.

Jacques, H. E., *How to Know the Insects*. Brown, 1947, 204 pp., $2.50.

Jacques, H. E., *How to Know the Trees*, Brown, 1946, 166 pp., $2.50.

Jacques, H. E., *Plant Families*, Brown, 1949, 177 pp., $2.50.

Jahn, T. L., *How to Know the Protozoa*, Brown, 1949, 234 pp., $3.00.

Kent, George C., Jr., *Comparative Anatomy of the Vertebrates*, C. V. Mosby, 1965, 550 pp., $9.25.

Kleiner, Israel S., and James M. Orten, *Human Biochemistry*, 5th ed., Mosby, 1965, 550 pp., $9.25.

Lane, Frank W., *Nature Parade: The Private Lives of Animals*, Premier D122, 1961, 272 pp., $.50.

Little, V. A., *General and Applied Entomology*, Harper, 1957, 543 pp., $7.00.

Margerson, David, *Medicine Today*, Penguin G29, 1961, 112 pp., $1.25.

Mason, A. Stewart, *Health and Hormones*, Penguin A487, 1960, 200 pp., $.95.

McElroy, William D., *Cellular Physiology and Biochemistry*, Prentice-Hall, 1961, 120 pp., $1.75.

Medawar, P. B., *The Future of Man*, Mentor MD331, 1961, 125 pp., $.50.

Milne, Lorus J., and J. G. Milne, *Plant Life*, Prentice-Hall, 1959, 283 pp., $6.95.

Milne, Lorus J., and Margery J. Milne, *The World of Night*, Explorer X15, 1960, 248 pp., $1.35.

Montagu, Ashley, *Human Heredity*, Mentor MT311, 1960, 364 pp., $.75.

Moore, Ruth, *Man, Time and Fossils*, Knopf, 1953, 411 pp., $6.50.

Morgan, Ann H., *Field Book of Ponds and Streams*, Putnam, 1930, 448 pp., $5.00.

Morholt, Evelyn and others, *Teaching High School Science: A Source Book for the Biological Sciences*, Harcourt, 1958, 506 pp., $6.75.

Osborn, Fairfield, *Our Plundered Planet*, Little, Brown, 1948, 217 pp., $3.50.

Paffenbarger, George C. (ed.), *Frontiers of Dental Science*, Scholastic, 1962, 160 pp., $.50.

Peattie, Donald Culross, *Flowering Earth*, Explorer X24, 1939, 252 pp., $1.45.

Peterson, Roger Tory, and James Fisher, *Wild America*, Houghton Mifflin, 1955, $5.00.

Pettingill, Olin, *Ornithology*, Burgess, 1958, 379 pp., $5.00.

Pfeiffer, John, *The Human Brain*, Worlds of Science No. I, 1962, 256 pp., $.75.

Platt, Rutherford, *1001 Answers to Questions About Trees*, Grosset and Dunlap 0807, 1959, 318 pp., $1.95.

Platt, Rutherford, *This Green World*, Dodd, 1942, 219 pp., $6.00.

Pohl, R. W., *How to Know the Grasses*, Brown, 1954, 192 pp., $2.75.

Poincare, Henri, *Science and Hypothesis*, Dover, 1952, 272 pp., $1.35.

Ramsay, J. A., *Physiological Approach to the Lower Animals*, Cambridge, 1962, 148 pp., $1.65.

Rhodes, Frank H. T., *The Evolution of Life*, Pelican A512, 1962, 302 pp., $1.45.

Riedman, Sarah R., *Our Hormones and How They Work*, Collier AS320, 1962, 127 pp., $.95

Sanderson, Ivan T., *Animal Treasure*, Explorer X25, 1961, 330 pp., $1.45.

Scheinfeld, Amram, *The Basic Facts of Human Heredity*, Washington Square W603, 1961, $.60.

Schmidt, Nielsen, *Animal Physiology*, Prentice-Hall, 1960, 118 pp., $1.75.

Sears, Paul B., *Where There Is Life*, Dell LC180, 1962, 224 pp., $.50.

Sheppard, P. M., *Natural Selection and Heredity*, Torchbooks TB528, 1960, 209 pp., $1.35.

Simpson, George Gaylord, *The Meaning of Evolution*, Yale Y23, 1960, 364 pp., $1.45.

Smith, Kenneth M., *Beyond the Microscope*, Pelican A119, 1957, 154 pp., $.95.

Sproul, Edith E., *The Science Book of the Human Body*, Cardinal C174, 1955, 232 pp., $.35.

Sterling, Dorothy, *Story of Mosses, Ferns, and Mushrooms*, Doubleday, 1955, $2.75.

Sussman, Maurice, *Animal Growth and Development*, Prentice-Hall, 1960, 114 pp., $1.75.

Swanson, Carl P., *The Cell*, Prentice-Hall, 1960, 114 pp., $1.75.

Tokay, Elbert, *The Human Body and How It Works*, New American Library, 1957, $.50.

Virchow, Rudolph, *Disease, Life, and Man*, Collier AS362X, 1962, 288 pp., $.95.

Von Frisch, Karl, *The Dancing Bees*, Harvest HB40, 1961, 182 pp., $1.95.

Von Koenigswald, G. H. R., *The Evolution of Man*, Ann Arbor 511, 1962, 148 pp., $1.95.

Waddington, C. H., *How Animals Develop*, Torchbooks TB553, 1962, 135 pp., $1.25.

Weaver, Richard L. (ed.), *Conservation Handbook*, National Association of Biology Teachers, 1955, 499 pp., $4.00.

Weisz, P. B., *The Science of Biology*, McGraw-Hill, 1959, 800 pp., $8.95.

White, Lancelot Law, *The Next Development in Man*, Mentor MP399, 1950, 254 pp., $.60.

Wilson, E. B., Jr., *Introduction to Scientific Research*, McGraw-Hill, 1953, 375 pp., $6.00.

Winchester, A. M., *Heredity and Your Life*, Dover T598, 1960, 333 pp., $1.45.

Zinsser, Hans, *Rats, Lice and History*, Bantam FC55, 1960, 228 pp., $.50.

Names and Addresses of Publishers

Abelard-Schuman, Ltd., 6 W. 57th St., New York, New York 10019
Affiliated Publishers, Inc., 630 Fifth Ave., New York, N.Y. 10020
Anchor—see Doubleday & Co.
Ann Arbor—The University of Michigan Press, Ann Arbor, Mich.
Apollo Editions, Inc., 425 Park Ave. South, New York, N.Y. 10016
Bantam Books, Inc., 271 Madison Ave., New York, N.Y. 10016
Barnes & Noble, Inc., 105 Fifth Ave., New York, N.Y. 10003
The Boxwood Press, P.O. Box 7171, Pittsburgh 13, Pa.
Wm. C. Brown Co., 135 S. Locust St., Dubuque, Iowa 52002
Burgess Pubiishing Company, 426 South 6th St., Minneapolis, Minn.
  55415
Cambridge University Press, 32 East 57th St., New York, N.Y. 10022
Cardinal—see Pocket Books.
College Outline—see Barnes & Noble.
Collier Books, 111 Fourth Ave. South, New York, N.Y. 10003
Compass—see Viking Press.
Thomas Y. Crowell Co., 201 Park Avenue South, New York, N.Y.
  10003
John Day Co., 200 Madison Ave., New York, N.Y. 10016
Dell Publishing Company, Inc., 750 Third Ave., New York, N.Y. 10017
Dial Press, Inc., 75 Third Ave., New York, N.Y. 10017
Dodd, Mead & Co., 432 Park Ave. So., New York, N.Y. 10016
Doubleday & Co., Inc., 575 Madison Ave., New York, N.Y. 10022
Dover Publications, Inc., 180 Varick St., New York, N.Y. 10014
Explorer—see Viking Press.
Fawcett Publications, Inc., 67 West 44th St., New York 36, N.Y.
Grosset & Dunlap, Inc., 1107 Broadway, New York, N.Y. 10010
Harper & Row, Publishers, Inc., 49 East 33rd St., New York, N.Y. 10016
Harvest—Harcourt, Brace & World, Inc., 750 Third Ave., New York,
  N.Y. 10017
Holt, Rinehart and Winston, Inc., 383 Madison Ave., New York, N.Y.
  10017
Houghton Mifflin Co., 2 Park Street, Boston, Mass. 02107
Alfred A. Knopf, Inc., 501 Madison Ave., New York, N.Y. 10022
Lantern Press, Inc., 257 Park Ave. So., New York, N.Y. 10010
Longmans, Green & Company, Ltd., 48 Grosvenor St., London, W.1
The Macmillan Company, 60 Fifth Ave., New York, N.Y. 10011
McGraw-Hill Book Co., Inc., 330 West 42nd St., New York, N.Y. 10036
Mentor—see New American Library.

Meridian—The World Publishing Co., 119 West 57th St., New York, N.Y. 10019
Minnesota—University of Minnesota Press, 2037 University Ave. S.E., Minneapolis, Minn. 55455
C. V. Mosby Co., 3207 Washington Blvd., St. Louis, Mo. 63103
National Association of Biology Teachers, P.O. Box 2113, Great Falls, Montana 59401
New American Library of World Literature, Inc., 501 Madison Ave., New York, N.Y. 10022
Pelican—see Penguin Books.
Penguin Books, Inc., 3300 Clipper Mill Road, Baltimore, Md. 21211
Pocket Books—see Affiliated Publishers, Inc.
Premier—see Fawcett Publications, Inc.
Prentice-Hall, Inc., Englewood Cliffs, N.J.
G. P. Putnam's Sons, 200 Madison Ave., New York, N.Y. 10016
Rand McNally & Co., Box 7600, Chicago, Ill. 60680
Random House, Inc., 457 Madison Ave., New York, N.Y. 10022
Scholastic Book Services, 904 Sylvan Ave., Englewood Cliffs, N.J.
Science Editions, 440 Park Ave. South, New York, N.Y. 10022
Signet Science—see New American Library.
Torchbooks—see Harper & Row.
Washington Square—see Affiliated Publishers, Inc.
John Wiley & Sons, Inc., 605 3rd Ave., New York, N.Y. 10016
Yale University Press, 149 York St., New Haven, Conn.

PROFESSIONAL PERIODICALS

There are a number of professional organizations, fraternities, or societies in the biological and related fields. Each such organization produces periodically some form of technical association journal. The assistant who is truly professionally oriented should keep abreast of various developments of significance to biology by reading and studying this professional literature from the societies.

Personal membership in professional societies is a real asset to the assistant. The department chairman or other teaching personnel can give information regarding the societies and can recommend the assistant for such organization memberships. On becoming a member by payment of dues, the assistant will generally receive the regular professional publication of the society. In other cases, the assistant may purchase the publication without establishing membership in the society.

The assistant can also become familiar with professional publications by spending regular time in the departmental or institutional library, reading selections from the various publications.

The assistant should become familiar with the following societies and the names of their publications. He should seek membership in such societies as those listed. He should encourage subscription to these publications by his departmental or institutional library. Information regarding membership and subscriptions may be obtained by writing directly to the organizations concerned.

Recommended Journal Publications of Professional Organizations

American Forests, The magazine of forests, soil, water, wildlife, and outdoor recreation, American Forestry Association, 919 17th Street, NW, Washington 6, D.C.

Audubon Magazine, National Audubon Society, 1130 Fifth Avenue, New York 28, New York.

Journal of Economic Entomology, Entomological Society of America, 4603 Calvert Road, College Park, Maryland.

Journal of Forestry, Society of American Forestry, Mills Bldg., 17th Street and Pennsylvania Avenue, NW, Washington 6, D.C.

Journal of Heredity, American Genetics Association, 1507 Main Street, NW, Washington 4, D.C.

Journal of Molecular Biology, Academic Press, Inc., 111 Fifth Avenue, New York 3, New York.

Journal of Paleontology, Society of Economic Paleontologists and Mineralogists, P.O. Box 979, Tulsa 1, Oklahoma.

Journal of the American Medical Association, 535 North Dearborn Street, Chicago 10, Illinois.

Journal of the American Dental Association, 222 East Superior Street, Chicago 11, Illinois.

Natural History, The Journal of the American Museum of Natural History, Central Park West at 79th Street, New York 24, New York.

Physics Today, American Institute of Physics, 335 E. 45th Street, New York 17, New York.

Plant Physiology, American Society of Plant Physiologists, Box 2665, University Station, Gainesville, Florida.

Plants and Gardens, Botanic Garden, 1000 Washington Avenue, Brooklyn 25, New York.

School Science and Mathematics, Central Association of Science and Mathematics Teachers, Oak Park, Illinois, monthly (9 months per year).

Science, American Association for the Advancement of Science, 1515 Massachusetts Avenue, N.W., Washington, D.C.

Science World, Scholastic Magazines, Inc., 33 West 42d Street, New York, New York.

Scientific American, Scientific American Inc., 415 Madison Avenue, New York, N.Y.

The American Anthropologist, American Anthropological Association, Logan Museum, Beloit, Wisconsin.

The American Biology Teacher, National Association of Biology Teachers, P.O. Box 2113, Great Falls, Montana, monthly (8 issues per year).

Tomorrow's Scientist, National Science Teacher's Association, 1201 16th Street NW, Washington 6, D.C., monthly (8 issues per year).

MUSEUMS, ZOOS, AQUARIA, BIOLOGICAL STATIONS, AND WILDLIFE REFUGES

Various public museums, zoos, aquaria, wildlife refuges, biological stations, and natural tourist attractions are located throughout the United States. These are generally developed and supported by local, state, or federal governments; some are connected with colleges or universities; others are developments of private individuals or foundations.

These agencies are excellent sources for providing technical information and for broadening the professional experience of the assistant. They demonstrate a wealth of plant and animal life as it appears in normal ecological relationships. They can usually be visited free of admission charge or for a small fee. They will effectively supplement any information gained by the assistant from textbooks, references, laboratory, or personal experiences during his formal education.

The assistant will have time for visiting such agencies during interquarter or semester breaks, summer vacation periods, or various holiday seasons. He can be sure of a great deal of recreational pleasure from his visits while at the same time increasing tremendously his knowledge and practical understanding of the organisms and ecological relationships of the biological world.

Many of these agencies supply free descriptive literature which the assistant may secure by writing to the addresses given. The assistant may also wish to inquire of the agency regarding summer employment opportunities. He can always be sure that serious acquaintance with such agencies will help him to grow in professional stature.

Museums

Albany, New York: New York State Museum.
Ann Arbor, Michigan: University of Michigan Mineralogy Museum.
Athens, Ohio: Ohio University Museum.
Atlanta, Georgia: Georgia State Museum.
Austin, Texas: Texas Memorial Museum.
Berkeley, California: University of California Museum of Vertebrate Zoology.
Boston, Massachusetts: Boston Museum of Science.
Boulder, Colorado: University of Colorado Museum.
Buffalo, New York: Buffalo Museum of Science.
Cambridge, Massachusetts: Harvard University Mineralogical Museum.
Chicago, Illinois: Chicago Natural History Museum.
Cleveland, Ohio: Cleveland Museum of Natural History.
Columbia, Missouri: University of Missouri Museum.
Denver, Colorado: Museum of Natural History.
Gainesville, Florida: Florida State University Museum.
Holbrook, Arizona: Petrified Forest National Museum.
Indianapolis, Indiana: Indiana State Museum.
Jefferson City, Missouri: Missouri Resources Museum.
Lawrence, Kansas: University of Kansas Museum of Natural History.
Lincoln, Nebraska: University of Nebraska State Museum.
Los Angeles, California: Los Angeles County Museum.
Miami, Florida: Museum of the Circus.
Montreal, Quebec: Redpath Museum.
New Haven, Connecticut: Peabody Museum of Natural History.
New Orleans, Louisiana: Louisiana State Museum.
New York, New York: American Museum of Natural History.
Ottawa, Ontario: Natural Museum of Canada.
Paterson, New Jersey: Paterson Museum.
Philadelphia, Pennsylvania: Academy of Natural Sciences.

Pittsburgh, Pennsylvania: Carnegie Institute Museum.
Rapid City, South Dakota: Museum of South Dakota School of Mines.
San Diego, Califronia: Natural History Museum.
San Francisco, California: California State Division of Mines Museum.
Santa Barbara, California: Santa Barbara Museum of Natural History.
Springfield, Illinois: Illinois State Museum.
Springfield, Massachusetts: Museum of Natural History.
Toronto, Ontario: Royal Ontario Museum of Geology and Mineralogy.
Trenton, New Jersey: State Museum of New Jersey.
University, Alabama: Alabama Museum of Natural History.
Urbana, Illinois: University of Illinois Museum of Natural History.
Vantage, Washington: Ginkgo Petrified Forest State Park Museum.
Washington, D. C.: U.S. National Museum and National Zoological Park.
Washington, D.C.: Smithsonian Institution.

Zoos

Atlanta, Georgia: Grant Park Zoo.
Birmingham, Alabama: Jimmy Morgan Zoo.
Chicago, Illinois: Chicago Zoological Society, Brookfield Zoo.
Chicago, Illinois: Lincoln Park Zoological Society.
Cincinnati, Ohio: Cincinnati Zoological Gardens.
Jacksonville, Florida: Jacksonville Zoo.
Miami, Florida: Cramden Park Zoo.
Miami, Florida: Monkey Jungle.
Miami, Florida: Serpentarium.
New York, New York: New York Zoological Society, Bronx Park.
Philadelphia, Pennsylvania: Philadelphia Zoological Park.
Pittsburgh, Pennsylvania: Highland Park Zoo.
Rock Creek, Washington: National Zoological Garden.
San Antonio, Texas: San Antonio Zoo.
San Diego, California: San Diego Zoological Society, Balboa Park.
San Diego, California: Zoological Park.
San Francisco, California: Fleischaker Zoo.
Sarasota, Florida: Sarasota Reptile Farm and Zoo.
Silver Springs, Florida: Ross Allen's Reptile Institute.
St. Louis, Missouri: St. Louis Zoological Garden, Forest Park.

Aquaria

Chicago, Illinois: Shedd Aquarium.
Key West, Florida: Municipal Aquarium.
Marineland, Florida: Marine Studios.

Philadelphia, Pennsylvania: Fairmount Park Aquarium.
San Francisco, California: Steinhart Aquarium.
Washington, D.C.: U.S. Fish and Wildlife Aquarium.

Biological Stations

Alligator Harbor, Florida: Oceanographic Institute.
Beaufort, North Carolina: Duke University Marine Laboratory.
Bloomfield Hills, Michigan: Cranbrook Institute of Science.
Boca Raton, Florida: Africa, U.S.A.
Butte, Montana: Montana School of Mines.
Cheboygan, Michigan: University of Michigan Biological Station, Douglas Lake.
Coral Gables, Florida: University of Miami Marine Laboratory.
Denver, Colorado: Colorado Bureau of Mines.
Everglades, Florida: Everglades National Park.
Friday Harbor, Washington: Friday Harbor Laboratories, University of Washington.
Homestead, Florida: The Orchid Jungle.
Houghton, Michigan: Michigan College of Mining and Technology.
Ithaca, New York: Cornell University, McGraw Hall.
Lake Itaska, Minnesota: University of Minnesota, Lake Itaska Biological Station.
La Jolla, California: Scripps Institute of Oceanography.
Miami, Florida: University of Miami Marine Laboratory.
Ocean Springs, Mississippi: Gulf Coast Research Laboratory.
Pacific Grove, California: Hopkins Marine Station.
Port Aransas, Texas: Institute of Marine Science.
Put-in-Bay, Ohio: Franz Stone Institute of Hydrobiology.
Seattle, Washington: University of Washington.
Socorro, New Mexico: New Mexico Institute of Mining and Technology.
Tucson, Arizona: University of Arizona.
Willis, Oklahoma: University of Oklahoma Biological Station, Lake Texoma.
Waycross, Georgia: Okefenokee Swamp Park.
Woods Hole, Massachusetts: Marine Biological Laboratory.

Wildlife Refuges

Bitter Lake Migratory Waterfowl Refuge, near Roswell, New Mexico.
Bosque del Apache National, Wildlife Refuge, at head of Elephant Butte Reservoir, New Mexico; waterfowl and fishing.

Cabeza Prieta Game Refuge, adjoining Organ Pipe Cactus National Monument, Arizona.

Desert Game Range, near Las Vegas, Nevada.

Imperial and Havasu National Wildlife Refuge, near Yuma, Arizona.

Kofa Game Refuge, near Yuma, Arizona.

Muleshoe National Wildlife Refuge, Northwest of Lubbock, Texas.

Safford National Wildlife Refuge, near Safford, Arizona.

Salt Plains National Wildlife Refuge, near Cherokee, Oklahoma.

Salt River National Wildlife Refuge, near Roosevelt, Arizona.

Salton Sea National Wildlife Refuge, at south end of Salton Sea, California.

San Andreas National Wildlife Refuge, West of White Sands National Monument, New Mexico.

THE ROLE OF THE ASSISTANT IN DEVELOPING THE DEPARTMENTAL PROGRAM IN HUMAN ANATOMY, PHYSIOLOGY, AND PATHOLOGY

Great numbers of the students who are enrolled in biological science courses are planning careers in nursing, pharmacy, medicine, hospital dietetics, hospital administration, laboratory technology, physiotherapy, the teaching of health and physical education or some related area. The assistant should take advantage of all information and teaching resources that will provide the most effective basic preparation for such students.

Sources of Assistance in Studying Normal Anatomy and Physiology

The following activities and sources of information will provide the assistant with the foundation of techniques and facts essential to a strong departmental program in human biology:

(1) Dissection of a variety of animal forms, such as the fetal pig and cat,

(2) Study of anatomical charts and models,

(3) References to pictorializations and diagrams in manuals of anatomy,

(4) Examination of isolated organs such as beef hearts and ox eyes that are obtained from biological supply houses,

(5) Review of anatomical atlases,

(6) Projection of biological and medical teaching slides,

(7) Procurement of a selection of motion pictures with anatomical, physiological, and pathological themes,

(8) Observations of a human cadaver in a cooperating school of medicine or dentistry,

(9) Observations and participation in autopsies with a cooperating hospital pathologist.

Normal Structures for Mastery by the Assistant in Directing Study of Human Anatomy and Physiology

The assistant should thoroughly familiarize himself with a broad selection of the anatomical structures of man, and he should learn the physiological functions of each structure. Such familiarity will require regular study and review of basic anatomy and physiology. He should consider himself generally responsible for directing student attention to such basic structures and their functions, and he should be able to discuss them intelligently with students. The student will thus gain (1) practical guidance for course credit examinations (2) opportunity to review formally and informally the general laboratory exercises and learnings in anatomy and physiology and (3) confident attention from the assistant regarding the specific body structures and functions encountered during various course experiences. The assistant must realize that a broad understanding of anatomy and physiology is fundamental to the study of pathology.

The ability to recognize and name the following structures and to recall their functions will permit the assistant to provide proper guidance for the students who demonstrate particular interest in human biology. The assistant should refer periodically to various written sources and specimens as he refreshes his understanding and tests his personal mastery of these anatomical and physiological groups.

The structures presented in each group may well serve as the source of specific questions to be asked on written and practical examinations for which students prepare under the guidance of the assistant.

Anatomical and Physiological Group I

Frontalis m.
Corrugator supercilii m.
Orbicularis oculi m.
Procerus m.
Nasalis m.

Infra-orbital portion of quadratus labii superioris m.
Zygomatic portion of quadratus labii superioris m.
Zygomatic m.

Triangularis m.
Caninus m.
Risorius m.
Mentalis m.
Quadratus labii inferioris m.
Dilatator naris m.
Depressor alae nasi m.
Auricularis anterior m.
Auricularis superior m.
Temporalis m.
Masseter m.
Buccinator m.
External pterygoid m.
Internal pterygoid m.
Occipitalis m.
Mylohyoid m.
Digastricus anterior m.
Digastricus posterior m.
Omohyoid m.
Geniohyoid m.
Scalenus anterior m.
Scalenus posterior m.
Scalenus medius m.
Platysma m.
Sternocleidomastoid m.
Trapezius m.
Splenius capitis m.
Sternothyroid m.
Sternohyoid m.
Styloglossus m.
Thyrohyoid m.
Stylopharyngeus m.
Stylohyoid m.
Ligamentum nucha
Ligamentum flavum
Anterior longitudinal ligament
Posterior longitudinal ligament
Intertransversus ligament

Interspinous ligament
Vertebral body
Vertebral foramen
Pedicle
Transverse process
Lamina
Spinous process
Demifacet for head of rib
Facet for tubercle of rib
Superior articular process
Inferior articular process
Inferior vertebral notch
Frontal bone
Temporal bone
Parietal bone
Ciliary arch
Zygomatic arch
Glabella
Nasal bone
Anterior nasal spine
Lacrimal bone
Ethmoid bone
Greater wing of sphenoid bone
Lesser wing of sphenoid bone
Perpendicular plate of ethmoid
Vomer
Nasal septum
Nasal cavity
Optic foramen
Orbicularis oris m.
Infra-orbital foramen
Mental foramen
Mandible
Maxilla
External occipital protuberance
Mastoid process
Styloid process

Anatomical and Physiological Group II

Superior concha
Middle concha
Inferior concha
Navicular (carpus)

Lunate
Triquetrum
Hamate
Pisiform

Capitate
Greater multangular
Lesser multangular
Navicular (tarsus)
Calcaneus
Talus
Cuboid
First cuneiform
Second cuneiform
Third cuneiform
Tendon
Muscle belly
Ligament
Synovial membrane
Superficial fascia
Deep fascia
Articular cartilage
Diaphysis
Epiphysis
Compact bone
Bone marrow
Medullary cavity
Endosteum
Periosteum
Anterior fontanel
Posterior fontanel
Right anterolateral fontanel
Left anterolateral fontanel
Right posterolateral fontanel
Left posterolateral fontanel
Frontal sinus
Maxillary sinus
Sphenoidal sinus
Ethmoidal sinus
Crista galli
Cribriform plate of the ethmoid bone
Orbital plate
Petrous portion of temporal bone
Anterior clinoid process

Middle clinoid process
Posterior clinoid process
Sella turcica
Foramen magnum
Anterior cranial fossa
Middle cranial fossa
Posterior cranial fossa
Superior orbital fissure
Optic foramen
Foramen spinosum
Foramen ovale
Foramen lacerum
Jugular foramen
Condylar foramen
Internal acoustic meatus
Sternal extremity
Coracoid tuberosity
Acromial extremity
Trapezius m. attachment to clavicle
Deltoid m. attachment to clavicle
Sternocleidomastoid m. attachment to clavicle
Pectoralis major m. attachment to clavicle
Subclavius m. attachment to clavicle
Sternohyoid m. attachment to clavicle
Head of rib
Neck of rib
Angle of rib
Shaft of rib
Tubercle of rib
Articular surfaces for vertebral bodies
Articular surface for transverse process of vertebra
Head of humerus
Neck of humerus
Surgical neck of humerus
Intertubercular groove
Greater tubercle of humerus

Anatomical and Physiological Group III

Lesser tubercle of humerus
Deltoid tuberosity
Groove for radial n.

Groove for ulnar n.
Lateral epicondyle
Medial epicondyle

Coronoid fossa
Olecranon fossa
Trochlea
Capitulum
Palatine process of maxilla
Incisive canal
Horizontal plate of palatine bone
Alveolar process
Zygomatic process of maxilla
Zygomatic bone

Zygomatic process of temporal bone
Mandibular fossa
Pterygoid hamulus
Posterior naris
Occipital condyle
Superior nuchal line
Inferior nuchal line
Foramen magnum
Palatine foramen
Carotid canal

Anatomical and Physiological Group IV

External intercostal m.
Pyramidalis m.
Gluteus medius m.
Gluteus maximus m.
Tensor fascia latae m.
Posterior gluteal line of innominate bone
Anterior gluteal line
Inferior gluteal line
Ilium
Posterior superior iliac spine
Tubercle of ilium
Posterior inferior iliac spine
Greater sciatic notch
Acetabular fossa
Ischial spine
Lesser sciatic notch
Ischium
Ischial tuberosity
Ischial ramus
Acetabular notch
Obturator foramen
Inferior pubic ramus
Pubic tubercle
Pubis
Obturator crest
Anterior superior iliac spine
Anterior inferior iliac spine
Pectin
Superior pubic ramus
Symphysical surface
Iliopectineal eminence

Arcuate line
Articular surface
Iliac crest
Iliac fossa
Promontory of sacrum
Ala
Pelvic sacral foramina
Sacral vertebra 1
Sacral vertebra 2
Sacral vertebra 3
Sacral vertebra 4
Sacral vertebra 5
Transverse ridges
Coccygeal vertebra 1
Coccygeal vertebra 2
Coccygeal vertebra 3
Coccygeal vertebra 4
Superior articular process
Sacral canal
Sacral tuberosity
Dorsal sacral foramina
Lateral sacral crest
Sacral horn
Coccygeal horn
Sacral hiatus
Middle sacral crest
Median sacral crest
Trochanteric fossa
Intertrochanteric crest
Head of femur
Neck of femur
Greater trochanter

Lesser trochanter
Intertrochanteric line
Gluteal tuberosity
Pectineal line
Spiral line
Shaft of femur
Linea aspera
Lateral epicondyle
Medial epicondyle
Lateral condyle

Medial condyle
Abductor tubercle
Intercondylar line
Intercondylar fossa
Subcutaneous surface of patella
Base of patella
Apex of patella
Facets for femoral condyles
Medial condyle of tibia
Lateral condyle of tibia

Anatomical and Physiological Group V

Intercondylar imminence
Nutrient foramen
Soleal line
Lateral surface
Interosseous border
Medial surface
Shaft of tibia
Anterior border
Medial border
Posterior surface of tibia
Medial malleolus of tibia
Malleolar sulcus of tibia
Apex of fibula
Head of fibula
Neck of fibula
Lateral surface
Medial surface
Lateral malleolus
Medial crest
Shaft of fibula
Interosseous border
Anterior border
Posterior surface
Posterior border
Right hypochondrium
Left hypochondrium
Epigastrium
Right lumbar region
Left lumbar region
Right iliac region
Left iliac region
Hypogastric region

Umbilical region
Pyloric antrum
Colic valve
Ampulla of Vater
Fundus of stomach
Cardia of stomach
Body of stomach
Pancreatic duct
Esophagus
Trachea
Right bronchus
Left bronchus
Thoracic aorta
Aortic arch
Abdominal aorta
Right liver lobe
Left liver lobe
Gall bladder
Greater omentum
Transverse colon
Sacculation of colon
Duodenum
Jejunum
Ileum
Caecum
Sigmoid colon
Rectum
Medial umbilical fold
Hepatic a.
Portal v.
Foramen of Winslow
Pylorus

Appendix
Duodenojejunal flexure
Pancreas
Stenson's duct
Parotid gland
Wharton's duct
Submaxillary gland
Epiglottis
Dorsum of tongue

Circumvallate papillae
Fungiform papillae
Filiform and conical papillae
Uvula
Isthmus faucium
Gingiva
Soft palate
Middle incisor
Lateral incisor

Anatomical and Physiological Group VI

Cuspid
First bicuspid
Second bicuspid
First molar
Second molar
Third molar
Pharyngeal tonsil
Dome of pleura
Right lung superior lobe
Right lung medial lobe
Right lung inferior lobe
Left lung superior lobe
Left lung inferior lobe
Cardiac notch
Falciform ligament of liver
Round ligament of liver
Hepatoduodenal ligament
Anterior pillar
Posterior pillar
Lingual tonsil
Rugae of stomach
Celiac axis
Cystic duct
Hepatic duct
Common bile duct
Tail of pancreas
Body of pancreas
Meso-appendix
Crown of tooth
Enamel
Dentine
Pulp cavity
Root

Alveolar process
Cementum
Periodental membrane
Posterior wall of pharynx
Brachioradialis m.
Palmaris longus m.
Flexor carpi ulnaris m.
Flexor carpi ulnaris m.
Extensor digitorum longus m.
Extensor digitorum communis m.
Gastrocnemius m.
Soleus m.
Tibialis anterior m.
Peroneus longus m.
Pectoralis major m. origin and insertion
Latissimus dorsi m. origin and insertion
Deltoid m. origin and insertion
Teres major m. origin and insertion
Supraspinatus m. origin and insertion
Infraspinatus m. origin and insertion
Trapezius m. origin and insertion
Serratus anterior m. origin and insertion
Biceps brachii m. origin and insertion
Triceps brachii m. origin and insertion
Palmaris longus m. origin and insertion
Rectus femoris m. origin and insertion
Gluteus maximus m. origin and insertion
Semimembranosus m. origin and insertion
Tensor fasciae latae m. origin and insertion
Abductor longus m. origin and insertion

Abductor brevis m. origin and insertion
Abductor magnus m. origin and insertion
Gracilis m. origin and insertion
Vastus lateralis m. origin and insertion
Sartorius m. origin and insertion
Biceps femoris m. origin and insertion
Gastrocnemius m. origin and insertion
Sternocleidomastoid m. origin and insertion
Splenius capitis m. origin and insertion

Platysma m. origin and insertion
External oblique m. origin and insertion
Right atrium
Left atrium
Right ventricle
Left ventricle
Coronary sinus
Inferior vena cava
Superior vena cava
Pulmonary aorta
Pulmonary a.

Anatomical and Physiological Group VII

Pulmonary v.
Systemic aorta
Aortic arch
Left subclavian a.
Right subclavian a.
Right common carotid a.
Left common carotid a.
Tricuspid valve
Bicuspid valve
Pulmonary semilunar valves
Aortic semilunar valves
Interatrial septum
Interventricular septum
Epicardium
Myodardium
Endocardium
Chordae tendineae
Papillary m.
Pericardium
Sinus of Valsalva
Coronary a.
Left border
Right border
Sternocostal surface
Apex of heart
Inferior border
Ascending aorta
Ligamentum arteriosum
Fossa ovalis
Musculi pectinati
Tricuspid orifice

Trabeculae carneae
Nodule
Lunule
Right innominate v.
Left innominate v.
Origin of coronary a.
Cusp of semilunar valve
Superior sagittal sinus
Sinus rectus
Plica vocalis
Plica ventricularis
Thyroid cartilage
Cavernous venous plexus
Superior petrosal sinus
Basilar a.
Vertebral a.
Inferior sagittal sinus
Trachea
Thoracic duct
Phrenic n.
Vagus n.
Bronchus
Bronchial a.
Costal pleura
Anterior tibial a.
Ascending aorta
Arcuate a.
Axillary a.
Brachial a.
Coeliac axis
Common carotid a.

Common iliac a.
Descending abdominal aorta
Descending thoracic aorta
Dorsalis pedis a.
External carotid a.
External iliac a.
Femoral a.
Inferior mesenteric a.
Innominate a.
Internal carotid a.
Internal iliac a.

Palmar arch
Posterior tibial a.
Popliteal a.
Radial a.
Renal a.
Spermatic a.
Ovarian a.
Subclavian a.
Superior mesenteric a.
Ulnar a.

Anatomical and Physiological Group VIII

Anterior tibial v.
Axillary v.
Azygous v.
Basilic v.
Cephalic v.
Common iliac v.
Cephalic v.
Dorsal venous arch
External jugular v.
Femoral v.
Great saphenous v.
Inferior vena cava
Innominate v.
Internal iliac v.
Internal jugular v.
Popliteal v.
Posterior tibial v.
Renal v.
Small saphenous v.
Subclavian v.
Superior vena cava
Ulnar v.
Portal v.
Splenic v.
Right colic v.
Superior mesenteric v.
Inferior mesenteric v.
Adenoid
Oropharynx
Larynx
Uvula

Inferior nasal meatus
Middle nasal meatus
Antrum of Highmore
Vomer bone
Perpendicular plate of ethmoid
Alveolus
Alveolar duct
Alveolar sac
Cricoid cartilage
Cartilaginous ring
Mediastinum
Abdominal aorta
Inferior vena cava
Kidney
Renal a.
Renal v.
Right common iliac a.
Right common iliac v.
Ureter
Urethra
Urinary bladder
Glomerulus
Renal Cortex
Renal medulla
Renal pelvis
Renal calyx
Proximal convuluted tubule
Distal convoluted tubule
Loop of Henle
Interlobar a.
Arcuate a.

Interlobular a.
Afferent arteriole
Efferent arteriole
Interlobular v.
Arcuate v.
Interlobar v.
Bowman's capsule
Collecting tubule
Renal pyramid
Renal column

Renal papilla
Testis
Scrotum
Epididymis
Vas deferens
Rectum
Prostate gland
Ejaculatory duct
Seminal vesicle

Anatomical and Physiological Group IX

Prostatic portion of urethra
Membranous portion of urethra
Cavernous portion of urethra
Glans penis
Prepuce
Symphysis pubis
Capsule of testis
Seminiferous tubule
Septum of testis
Lobule of testis
Fundus of uterus
Body of uterus
Ovary
Round ligament
Uterosacral ligament
Anterior ligament of uterus
Posterior ligament of uterus
Broad ligament
Cervix
Vagina
Cervical canal
Anterior fornix
Lateral fornix
Posterior fornix
Fimbriated end of fallopian tube
Perineum
Cul-de-sac of Douglas
Body cavity of uterus
External os
Internal os
Immature Graafian follicle
Mature Graafian follicle

Pectoralis m.
Rib
Skin of mammary gland
Adipose tissue
Ampulla
Areola
Areolar glands
Lactiferous duct
Nipple
Pituitary gland
Pineal gland
Anterior lobe of pituitary gland
Intermediate lobe of pituitary gland
Posterior lobe of pituitary gland
Thyroid gland
Parathyroid gland
Pancreas
Thymus gland
Adrenal gland
Stomach mucosa
Duodenal mucosa
Placenta
Liver
Cricoid cartilage
Arytenoid cartilage
Thyroid cartilage
Superior thyroid a.
Trachea
Common carotid a.
Vagus n.
Internal jugular v.
Inferior thyroid a.

Sphenoid sinus
Cavernous sinus
Pons
Optic chiasma
Zona glomerulosa of adrenal
Zona fasciculata of adrenal
Zona reticularis of adrenal
Adrenal capsule
Adrenal cortex
Pancreatic alveolus

Pancreatic islet of Langerhans
Superior parathyroid gland
Inferior parathyroid gland
Spermatic cord
Ampulla of vas deferens
Anus
Penis
Tubuli recti
Rete testis

Anatomical and Physiological Group X

Efferent ductules
Spermatogonium
Undifferentiated germ cell
Primary spermatocyte
Secondary spermatocyte
Spermatid
Spermatozoon
Peritoneum
Seminal vesicle
Vaginal orifice
Skene's glands
Bartholin's glands
Cowper's gland
Labia majora
Labia minora
Vestibule
Hymen
Urinary orifice
Sacral promontory
Ampulla of uterine tube
Suspensory ligament of ovary
Mesosalpinx
Corpus luteum
Corpus albicans
Corpus cavernosum penis
Corpus spongiosum penis
Ureteral orifice
Trigone of urinary bladder
Node of Ranvier
Neurilemma
Axis cylinder
Medullary sheath

Dura mater
Pia mater
Arachnoid
Subdural space
Decussation of the pyramids
Cervical enlargement of cord
Lumbar enlargement of cord
Conus medullaris
Filum terminale
Cauda equina
Posterior median sulcus
Posterior median septum
Posterior lateral sulcus
Anterior median fissure
Posterior nerve root
Anterior nerve root
Anterior column of gray matter
Intermediate column of gray matter
Posterior column of gray matter
Central canal of spinal cord
Spinal ganglion
Posterior division of spinal n.
Cerebellum
Pons
Frontal lobe
Parietal lobe
Temporal lobe
Occipital lobe
Cerebrum
Medulla oblongata
Cerebral peduncle
Olfactory tract

Optic n.
Optic chiasma
Mamillary body
Posterior medullary velum
Anterior medullary velum
Choroid plexus
Corpora quadrigemina
Superior colliculus of corpora quadrigemina
Inferior colliculus of corpora quadrigemina

Fourth ventricle
Corpus callosum
Genu
Splenium
Fornix
Septum lucidum
Foramen of Monro
Third ventricle
Pineal body
Aqueduct of Sylvius

Anatomical and Physiological Group XI

Pituitary body
Fissure of Rolando
Fissure of Sylvius
Anterior central gyrus
Posterior central gyrus
Superior temporal gyrus
Inferior temporal gyrus
Superior frontal gyrus
Middle frontal gyrus
Inferior frontal gyrus
Subarachnoid space
Thalamus
Olfactory n.
Anterior cerebral a.
Posterior cerebral a.
Middle cerebral a.
Vertebral a.
Internal carotid a.
Anterior gray commissure
Posterior gray commissure
Anterior funiculus
Lateral funiculus
Posterior funiculus
Fasciculus gracilis
Fasciculus cuneatus
Periorbital fat
Lateral rectus eye m.
Medial rectus eye m.
Superior oblique eye m.
Inferior oblique eye m.
Lacrimal gland

Hard palate
Occipital bone
Nasal bone
Cribriform plate of ethmoid bone
Right cerebral hemisphere
Left cerebral hemisphere
Longitudinal fissure
Cervical segment of cord
Thoracic segment of cord
Lumbar segment of cord
Sacral segment of cord
Axon
Dendrite
Nucleus
Nerve cell body
Anterior horn of lateral ventricle
Choroid plexus of lateral ventricle
Choroid plexus of third ventricle
Inferior horn of lateral ventricle
Insula
Claustrum
Putamen
Globus pallidus
Caudate nucleus
Thalamus
Internal capsule
Hippocampus
Lentiform nucleus
Visual receptive center
Olfactory center
Fasciculus cuneatus

Fasciculus gracilis
Dorsal spinocerebellar tract
Ventral corticospinal tract
Ventral spinothalamic tract
Ventral spinocerebellar tract
Lateral spinothalamic tract
Lateral corticospinal tract
Rubrospinal tract
Posterior horn of lateral ventricle
Arbor vitae
Olfactory n. I

Optic n. II
Oculomotor n. III
Trochlear n. IV
Trigeminal n. V
Abducent n. VI
Facial n. VII
Acoustic n. VIII
Glossopharyngeal n. IX
Vagus n. X
Accessory n. XI

Anatomical and Physiological Group XII

Hypoglossal n. XII
Anterior cutaneous n.
Lateral cutaneous n.
Posterior cutaneous n.
Sulcomarginal fasciculus
Septomarginal fasciculus
Vestibulospinal fasciculus
Olivospinal fasciculus
Tectospinal fasciculus
Reticulospinal fasciculus
Semilunar ganglion
Ophthalmic division of trigeminal n.
Maxillary division of trigeminal n.
Mandibular division of trigeminal n.
Brachial plexus
Sciatic n.
Tibial n.
Common peroneal n.
Cervical plexus
Medial rectus m.
Lumbosacral plexus
Superior rectus m.
Inferior rectus m.
Lateral rectus m.
Association fibers of brain
Projection fibers of brain
Commissural fibers of brain
Auditory receptive center
Epineurium
Perineurium
Endoneurium

Axillary n.
Median n.
Musculocutaneous n.
Radial n.
Ulnar n.
Nasal mucosa
Superior turbinate
Middle turbinate
Inferior turbinate
Optic foramen
Retina
Rod cell
Cone cell
Lateral geniculate body
Medial geniculate body
Midbrain
Oculomotor nucleus
Preganglionic fibers
Postganglionic fibers
Sensory nucleus of cranial n. V
Motor nucleus of cranial n. V
Nucleus of cranial n. VII
Semicircular canals
Jugular ganglion
Nodose ganglion
Hypoglossal nucleus
Medial lemniscus
Lateral lemniscus
Nucleus gracilis
Nucleus cuneatus
Optic n.

Central artery of retina
Fovea centralis
Optic nerve sheath
Anterior chamber
Crystalline lens
Conjunctiva
Sclera
Choroid
Hyaloid canal
Vitreous body

Iris
Posterior chamber
Caruncula lacrimalis
Punctum lacrimale
Ductus lacrimalis
Saccus lacrimalis
Ductus nasolacrimalis
Inferior nasal meatus
Lacrimal gland
Lacrimal ducts

Pathological Conditions for Mastery by the Assistant in Directing Study of Human Pathology

Added to his acquaintance with normal anatomy and physiology the assistant should develop an understanding of a selection of pathological conditions of various body systems. The assistant's knowledge of these diseases will enable him to (1) logically relate the normal anatomy and physiology to the abnormal pathology (2) analyze with students the nature of the processes of pathology (3) motivate appreciation for the normal by stressing the abnormal and (4) introduce his students to pathological conditions about which little may be known at present.

Understanding of the following conditions will constitute an effective store of knowledge of pathology for the assistant:

The Integumentary System
Acne
Blackheads
Rash
Hives
Boils
Ringworms
Warts
Leprosy
Lipoma
Squamous epithelioma
Dandruff
Baldness

The Muscular System
Atrophy
Hypertrophy
Rigor mortis

Tetanus
Fatigue
Poliomyelitis
Flaccid paralysis
Spastic paralysis
Muscular dystrophy

The Skeletal System
Sprains
Dislocations
Arthritis
Torn cartilage
Simple fracture
Compound fracture
Scoliosis
Slipped disc

The Digestive System
Dysphagia

Cardiospasm
Indigestion
Gastritis
Peptic Ulcer
Cancer
Gallstones
Jaundice
Appendicitis
Constipation
Hemorrhoids
Diarrhea
Flatulence
Obesity

The Circulatory System

Arteriosclerosis
Apoplexy
Edema
Elephantiasis
Tachycardia
Cardiac Hypertrophy
Coronary thrombosis
"Blue babies"
Mitral stenosis
Aortic regurgitation
Congestive heart failure
Erythroblastosis fetalis
Leukemia
Leucocytosis
Leucopenia
Hemophilia
Anemia
Hypertension
Adenitis
Lymphangitis

The Respiratory System

Asphyxia
Mountain sickness
Pyothorax
Hemothorax
Pneumothorax
Hydrothorax
Common cold
Diphtheria

Tuberculosis
Sinusitis
Asthma
Pleurisy
Apnea
Dyspnea
Cheyne-Stokes breathing
Orthopnea
Pulmonary embolism

The Endocrine System

Organ atrophy
Hirsutism
Addison's disease
Cretinism
Exophthalmic goiter
Myxedema
Tetany
Diabetes mellitus
Diabetes insipidus
Dwarfism
Acromegaly
Giantism
Ketosis
Froelich's syndrome

The Excretory System

Polyuria
Dysuria
Oliguria
Anuria
Retention
Incontinence
Supression
Nephritis
Pyuria
Renal calculi
Hematuria
Glycosuria

The Reproductive System

Syphilis
Gonorrhea
Abortion
Miscarriage

Eclampsia
Ectopic pregnancy
Sterility
Involutional melancholia
Amenorrhea
Menorrhagia
Dysmenorrhea
Prostatitis
Cryptorchidism
Postpartum hemorrhage
Inguinal hernia

The Nervous System

Tumors
Meningitis
Epilepsy
Neuroses
Psychoses

Syringomyelia
Migraine headache
Referred pain
Nymphomania
Frigidity
Satyriasis

The Special Senses

Conjunctivitis
Cataract
Astigmatism
Color-blindness
Strabismus
Glaucoma
Otitis media
Transmission deafness
Perception deafness
Central deafness

THE HOSPITAL PATHOLOGY LABORATORY
AS A SPECIALIZED LEARNING FACILITY

Medical and dental schools of course have cadavers for study by advanced students. Unfortunately, the college biology student too often has no opportunity to observe firsthand the real anatomy of the human organism to which he devotes months of study from the college textbook.

Despite this scarcity of school experiences with cadavers, most cities have hospitals, and these hospitals, especially in the larger cities and towns, have departments of pathology whose personnel the assistant will generally find most cooperative in aiding with the college program of studies.

The assistant will discover that a hospital pathologist can be a willing source of help in arranging unique observation and participation experiences for graduate and undergraduate biology students. Such a pathologist will demonstrate and discuss for the assistant, the professor, and their students the items generally included in preparing the report of the autopsy. He will interpret his check list of specific features observed as he dissects and studies the body to determine the causes of death and will present the microscopic aspects of the postmortem. He will also demonstrate the techniques of composing and dictating a final report for the official files as he verifies the factors precipitating the death of the patient.

Items in the Written Autopsy Protocol
Date and hour patient died:
Date and hour of autopsy:
Names of prosector and assistant:
Indication of whether full autopsy, head only, or trunk only:
Clinical diagnosis:
Pathological diagnosis:
Approved signature:
Age, sex, autopsy number:
Name, case number, ward number:
Provisional anatomical diagnoses:
Abstract of clinical history:
External examination findings:
Visceral cavities described, including pleural, peritoneal, pericardial:
General findings from the cardiovascular, respiratory, biliary, GI, GU, lymphatic, endocrine, nervous, and skeletal systems:
Description of findings involving pancreas and spleen:

The Protocol of Findings from Cadaver Examination
The hospital pathologist is naturally in excellent position to routinely apply his knowledge of anatomy and physiology to a detection of abnormal pathological processes which cause death. By careful observation of the cadaver before and during the postmortem dissection, he is able to comprehensively describe the condition of various organs of the body.

Dissection requires meticulous observation of the external and internal body features. For example, as a part of the postmortem examination the pathologist notes such features as the conjunctivae of the eyes. He describes whether they are normal, pale, icteric, injected, or hemorrhagic. He then notes whether the tonsils are present or absent and whether they are atrophied or hypertrophied. He observes the pleural cavities to determine if they are normal, obliterated, empty, or filled to some degree with fluid that may be serofibrinous, fibrinopurulent, or hemorrhagic. He notes whether the common bile duct is normal, patent, compressed, occluded, or distended. He views the stomach serosa and decides if it is normal, opaque, rough, or marked by exudate. The urinary bladder may be found to be normal, collapsed, fibrosed, or distended. The striations of the kidney medulla are described as distinct or indistinct. The pathologist notes also the distinction or lack of distinct appearances of the corticomedullary junctions.

This process of observation and description of findings from examining numerous body organs enables the pathologist to write a formal comprehensive report called an "autopsy protocol." The assistant should study the representative protocols which follow, keeping in mind that they represent (1) comprehensive knowledge of normal anatomy and physiology (2) mastery of pathological processes (3) the ability to observe carefully (4) the necessity for providing written records of scientific observations (5) skill in applying the scientific vocabulary (6) the practice of drawing conclusions as to the causes of death and (7) the anatomy, physiology, and pathology of body structures that are considered in biology laboratories by the assistant and the students who study under his guidance.

Representative Written Autopsy Protocol A

a. External and Internal Examination and Gross Findings—
Autopsy A

External Examination: The body is that of a well developed, well nourished, elderly female. Rigor mortis is slightly present throughout and livor mortis is not well visualized. The body has been embalmed. There is a recent laceration made approximately 1 to 2 cm. in diameter in the right forehead. There are diffuse ecchymotic areas around the eye in the right side and around the right shoulder. No tumor is palpated about the breast. The abdomen is slightly globoid. The external genitalia are not remarkable. The lower and superior extremities are grossly not remarkable.

Internal Examination: The body is opened by the usual "Y" shaped incision. The peritoneal cavity contains no fluid. The peritoneum is grayish white and glistening. The main abdominal organs are in their normal position. The inferior edge of the liver is at the level of the right costal margin in the midclavicular line. Both pleural cavities are grayish white. There is no evidence of pleural adhesions or effusions. The pericardium is yellowish gray. The pericardial sac contains no fluid. The abdominal cavity is moderately distorted due to previous embalming procedure.

Heart and Great Vessels: The heart weighs approximately 300 gms. The vessels entering and leaving the heart are natural. The coronary arteries, right and left, show scattered atheromatous plaques within the intima, but the lumina are widely patent. The tricuspic, pulmonic, aortic, and mitral valves are within normal limits and not remarkable. The right ventricle is 0.3 cm. in thickness; the left ventricle is 1.5 cm. in thickness. The aorta and its main branches show arteriosclerotic changes throughout. The superior and inferior vena cavae, splenic, and portal veins are natural.

Organs of the Neck and Mediastinum: The thyroid is natural. The trachea is patent. The tracheo-bronchial lymph nodes are grossly not remarkable.

Lungs: Both lungs are similar. The main pulmonary arteries are filled with organized thrombotic material. The parenchyma is markedly edematous in either side. The bronchi are slightly filled with a moderate amount of mucoid material. The lungs are slightly increased in consistency.

Liver, Gallbladder and Biliary Tree: The liver is of normal size and shape. The parenchyma is congested. The lobular pattern is indistinct. The gallbladder and biliary tree are natural.

Spleen: The spleen is normal in size and shape. The pulp is reddish brown.

G. I. System: The G. I. tract is grossly not remarkable. The stomach and small intestine are distorted by previous puncture due to embalming procedure. The appendix and large intestine are natural.

Pancreas: The pancreas is of normal size and shape. The parenchyma is moderately infiltrated by fatty tissue.

Adrenals: The adrenals are of normal size and shape. On section they are autolytic. The cortices are thin and golden yellow.

G. U. System: Both kidneys are similar. The left kidney contains several large retention cysts filled with a clear fluid and measuring approximately up to 4 cm. in diameter. On section the capsule strips with ease, leaving a brown surface with scattered pyelonephritic scars. The cortico-medullary relationship is fairly well defined. The kidneys are otherwise not remarkable. The ureters are patent. The uterus, fallopian tubes, and ovaries are grossly not remarkable. The urinary bladder is congested. *Bone Marrow:* The bone marrow is reddish brown.

Head: The head is opened in the usual fashion. The bones are natural. The subcutaneous tissues are moderately congested around the frontal region. The brain weighs 1500 gms. The vessels of the Circle of Willis show arteriosclerotic changes. The arteries appear patent. The brain is swollen throughout and moderately congested. The cerebral hemispheres are symmetrical. There is a slight conization of the cerebellar tonsils. The pons and cerebellum are grossly not remarkable. The brain is fixed; further sections will be taken. The pituitary gland is grossly not remarkable.

b.   Microscopic Description—Autopsy A

Lungs: The lungs exhibit areas of atelectasis and emphysema. The pulmonary vessels are congested throughout. A moderate amount of a pinkish staining fluid is present in some areas within the alveolar spaces. In addition, focal areas of anthracosis are noted. The pulmonary arteries are filled with an organized thrombus which occupies their entire lumina.

Heart: There is a slight fragmentation of the myocardial muscle fibers. In addition, focal areas of fibrosis are present.

Coronary Arteries: Sections from the right coronary arteries reveal atheromatous plaques within the intima. These are composed of cholesterol clefts and focal areas of calcification. The lumen is widely patent.

Adrenals: The cortical cells exhibit a moderate lipoid depletion. The adrenals are slightly congested.

Pancreas: The interstitial tissue is being replaced by fat in large areas. The pancreatic tissue cells are slightly autolytic.

Spleen: The spleen is markedly congested throughout. It also appears focally hemorrhagic.

Kidneys: The glomeruli are slightly increased in cellularity. The tubules are poorly preserved. The vessels are congested throughout. The interstitial tissue is focally infiltrated by lymphocytes.

c. Gross Brain Description—Autopsy A
Examination of the brain after fixation reveals symmetrical hemispheres. The cerebellum and pons are natural except for a slight conization of the cerebellar tonsils. There is slight swelling of the brain.
Coronal sections throughout the brain reveal moderate congestion. There is an old ischemic infarct of the left lentiform nucleus involving also part of the white matter. It measures approximately 4 x 1 cm. The vessels of the Circle of Willis exhibit marked atheromatous changes. It is nodular in appearance; the lumena of the arteries are narrow.

d. Microscopic Description of Brain—Autopsy A
Sections of the lentiform nucleus reveal a large surrounding cystic area. The parenchyma shows marked feathery degeneration and large areas of liquefaction necrosis. A few foamy histiocytes are present.

e. Abstract of Clinical History—Autopsy A
The patient was admitted on 6/14/62. She fell and injured the right side of her forehead. Apparently she had lost some blood. The blood pressure was 80/60 and the pulse 100. Stimulation therapy was applied. An X-ray of the skull showed no evidence of fracture. The white blood cell count was 11,000— 80% neutrophiles and 20% lymphocytes. Hemoglobin 11.0 and hematocrit 39.
Physical examination on surgical ward revealed a temporal hematoma. Blood pressure 140/70, 3 + pedal edema present in the extremities. Patient was semi-comatose and violent at times. The neurological examination revealed deep stupor. The patient does not speak. Right hemiparesis. Questionable Babinski reflex, withdraws left hand when right is pricked.

f. Clinical Diagnoses (including operations)
1. C.V.A., left side

    2. Right Hemiparesis with Facial Involvement

    3. Stupor

g. Final Diagnoses from Autopsy A

    RESPIRATORY SYSTEM:

          1. Massive Pulmonary Thrombo-Embolism.

          2. Pulmonary Edema, severe.

    CARDIOVASCULAR SYSTEM:

          1. Coronary Atherosclerosis.

          2. Generalized Arteriosclerosis.

    GLANDULAR SYSTEM:

          1. Moderate Congestion of Liver.

          2. Autolysis of Adrenal.

    G. U. SYSTEM:

          1. Retention Cysts of Left Kidney.

          2. Chronic Pyelonephritis.

    CENTRAL NERVOUS SYSTEM:

          1. Swelling of Brain.

          2. Old Ischemic Infarct involving the Lentiform Nucleus and White Matter.

          3. Severe Arteriosclerosis of Basal Arteries.

    MISCELLANEOUS:

          1. Hematoma of Right Forehead.

          2. Ecchymotic areas around Right Eye and Right Shoulder.

Representative Written Autopsy Protocol B

a. External and Internal Examination and Gross Findings—Autopsy B

External Examination: The body is that of a well developed, fairly well nourished, elderly male. Rigor mortis is present throughout; livor mortis is present in the posterior aspect of the body. The height is 5'8", and the estimated weight is 120

pounds. The head is covered by gray hair. There is no evidence of trauma. The conjunctivae and sclerae are grayish white. No fluid is exuding from ears, nose, or mouth. The neck is natural. The chest is slightly increased in the anterior-posterior diameter. The abdomen is scaphoid. The external genitalia are natural. The lower and superior extremities are natural.

Internal Examination: The body is opened by the usual "Y" shaped incision. The peritoneal cavity contains no fluid. The main abdominal organs are in their normal position. There is no evidence of peritoneal adhesions. The right and left pleural cavities contain no fluid. There are some thin fibrous adhesions between the perietal and visceral pleura. The pericardium is yellowish gray. The pericardial sac contains about 10 cc. of a yellow clear fluid.

Heart and Great Vessels: The heart weighs 330 gms. The vessels entering and leaving the heart are in their normal position. The chambers of the heart are moderately dilated. The tricuspic, pulmonic, aortic, and mitral valves are within normal limits and not remarkable. The myocardium is reddish brown in color and moderately firm in consistency. The left ventricle is 1.7 cm. in thickness and the right venticle is 0.4 cm. in thickness. There is an area of myocardial infarct, old, measuring approximately 5 x 3 cm. in the anterior septal aspect of the left ventricle. The ventricular wall is thinned out; the myocardial muscle fibers are replaced by a grayish-white, firm, fibrous tissue. The endocardial surface is depressed and covered by an old organized thrombus, firmly adherent to the endocardial surface, measuring 2.5 cm. in diameter. The left coronary artery and its main branches, anterior, descending, and circumflex, show marked arteriosclerotic changes with marked thickening of the wall and narrowing of the lumena. The right coronary artery shows arteriosclerotic changes but of a lesser degree. The aorta and its main branches show marked arteriosclerotic changes throughout with large areas of calcification. The superior and inferior vena cavae, splenic, and portal veins are natural.

Organs of the Neck and Mediastinum: The thyroid gland is

natural. The trachea is patent. The mucosa is slightly congested. The tracheo-bronchial lymph nodes are natural.

Lungs: Both lungs are similar. The pleurae are grayish white. On section the parenchyma reveals scattered areas of consolidation which are pale gray and friable. The parenchyma exhibits also moderate congestion and edema. The upper lobe in either side shows marked emphysematous changes. The bronchi are partially filled with a thick mucoid fluid. The pulmonary vessels are natural.

Liver: The liver weighs 1500 gms. The external surface is smooth and glistening. On section the lobular pattern is indistinct. The liver is normal in consistency.

Gallbladder and Biliary Tree: The gallbladder and biliary ducts are natural.

Spleen: The spleen is moderately enlarged, weighing 250 gms. The capsule is thickened in places, with areas of hyalinization. The pulp is soft; the lymphoid follicles and trabeculae are indistinct.

G. I. System: The esophageal mucosa is natural. The stomach is of normal size and shape. The stomach contains a moderate amount of undigested food. The mucosa shows no evidence of erosion, tumor, or ulcer. The small intestine, appendix vermiformis, and large intestine are natural.

Pancreas: The pancreas is yellowish tan and firm. The pancreatic duct is patent. There is a moderate fatty infiltration of the parenchyma.

Adrenals: Both adrenals are similar. The cortices are thickened and nodular. They are golden yellow in color.

G.U. System: Both kidneys are similar. They weigh 100 gms. each. The capsule strips with slight difficulty, leaving a granular brown surface. On section the cortico-medullary relationship is well defined. The cortices are thin. The calyceal system, pelves, and papillae are natural. The patent ureters are of normal size. The bladder is of normal size and shape. The mucosa is trabeculated. The prostate gland is moderately enlarged and composed of yellowish gray nodules embedded in white fibrous tissue. The seminal vesicles are natural. The testes are of normal size and shape. On section the parenchyma is tan and soft; it strings with difficulty.

Bone Marrow: The bone marrow is reddish brown.

Head: The head is opened in the usual fashion. The scalp is reflected. The subcutaneous tissue and bones are natural. The dura mater is not remarkable. The brain weighs 1300 gms. The cerebral hemispheres are symmetrical. The cerebellum and pons are natural. The vessels of the Circle of Willis show marked arteriosclerotic changes.

Pituitary Gland: Natural.

b. Microscopic Examination—Autopsy B

Lungs: Sections of the lungs reveal areas of emphysema. In places there are large collections of polys and a pinkish staining fluid present within the alveolar spaces. The pulmonary arterioles exhibit a marked fibro-thickening of their walls.

Heart: Sections of the heart, from areas of previous infarct, exhibit a hyalinized fibrous tissue replacing a large number of myocardial fibers. Elsewhere the myocardial fibers are within normal limits. The nuclei are fairly uniform. The epicardial fatty tissue is mildly infiltrated by lymphocytes. In one of the sections a segment of an organized thrombus is present in the endocardial surface.

Coronary arteries: Sections of the coronary arteries reveal marked fibro-thickening of the intima with large atheromatous plaques and large areas of calcification. The lumen contains a re-canalized, fairly recent thrombus.

Spleen: The lymphoid follicles are poorly demarcated. The central arterioles are thickened and dilated.

Liver: The liver is fairly well preserved. The hepatic cells show vacuolated nuclei. The cytoplasm is eosinophilic and indistinct. The sinusoids and central veins are moderately engorged. The portal spaces are mildly infiltrated by lymphocytes and show no unusual changes.

Adrenals: The cortex is nodular and somewhat hyperplastic. The cells have a normal amount of lipoid content. The medulla is not well visualized. The adrenal veins are moderately congested.

Kidneys: The interstitial tissue is focally infiltrated by lymphocytes. Some of the glomeruli are hyalinized. The distal tubules contain hyaline casts. The arteries show a laminated, thickened wall.

Pancreas: The pancreas shows some autolytic changes; otherwise it appears histologically not remarkable. The pancreatic arteries show a moderate thickening of their walls.

c. Abstract of Clinical History—Autopsy B

Patient had generalized arteriosclerosis. He became gradually bedridden and stuporous.

Patient followed a progressive down-hill course and expired.

d. Clinical Diagnoses (including operations)
   1. Chronic Myocarditis

e. Final Anatomical Diagnoses from Autopsy B

RESPIRATORY SYSTEM:

1. Acute Bilateral Bronchopneumonia.
2. Moderate Pulmonary Emphysema.
3. Old Pleural Adhesions.

CARDIOVASCULAR SYSTEM:

1. Coronary Arteriosclerotic Heart Disease.
2. Coronary Sclerosis, severe.
3. Old Coronary Thrombosis, anterior descending branch.
4. Old Antero-Septal Myocardial Infarct of Left Ventricle.
5. Mural Thrombus of Left Ventricle.
6. Generalized Arteriosclerosis.

GLANDULAR SYSTEM:

1. Passive Congestion of Liver.
2. Nodular Hyperplasia of Adrenal Glands.
3. Fatty Infiltration of Pancreas.

SPLEEN & HEMATOPOIETIC:

1. Chronic Perisplenitis.

G. U. SYSTEM:

1. Nephrosclerosis.
2. Chronic Cystitis.
3. Benign Prostatic Hyperplasia.

CENTRAL NERVOUS SYSTEM:

1. Arteriosclerosis of Basal Arteries.

Chapter III
Materials, Supplies, and Equipment

PURPOSES

1. To outline for the assistant the types of materials, supplies, and equipment generally required for the biology student,

2. To provide the assistant a number of sources of materials, supplies, and equipment for departmental and personal use,

3. To instruct the assistant in the use of various instruments utilized in the department and in the laboratory,

4. To provide general guidelines in the care and maintenance of materials and various items of equipment.

GENERAL USE AND CARE OF EQUIPMENT

Property of considerable value is placed in the hands of students engaged in the biology program of studies. This property must be used carefully and cared for adequately.

The same microscopes, slide collections, and other equipment are often used by different students in successive laboratory sections. If any equipment assigned to a student is damaged or missing at the beginning of a laboratory period, this fact should be reported at once to the assistant so that a charge may be placed against the previous user. Materials damaged while being used by a student must also be reported immediately. Crushing or breaking a prepared microscope slide may involve a charge of 50 cents to $2.50, depending upon the actual cost of replacement. The assistant should determine with the department head the actual costs to be assessed for breakage or damage to equipment in general.

MATERIALS AND SUPPLIES GENERALLY
REQUIRED BY THE STUDENT

Each biology student will have occasion to use and care for such items as those which follow. The assistant should be familiar with the sources, costs, quality, and general storage placement of these items. In some cases, the items will be furnished by the department. In other cases, the student may be required to furnish his own.

(1) Textbook (title and author to be announced) and laboratory manual to be assigned by the professor.

(2) One dissecting set, consisting of two dissecting needles, one scalpel, one pair of dissecting forceps, one pair of scissors, a probe, one curved forceps, one straight forceps, one hand lens or tripod.

(3) One celluloid ruler graduated in millimeters, one 4H drawing pencil, one 3H or any soft-lead pencil, colored pencils (blue, red, green, and brown), one eraser with beveled ends (not art gum), and three pieces of emery paper or sandpaper.

(4) Ruled note paper, plain note paper, a quantity of drawing paper, and one large manila envelope.

(5) One hand towel, Bunsen burners, reagent bottles, Petri dishes, filter paper, beakers, test tubes, test tube holders, Syracuse watch glasses, flat-bottomed vials, toothpicks, steel pins, safety razor blades, pipettes.

(6) Binocular microscope, wide-field microscope, compound microscope, microscope slides 1 x 3 inches, microscope cover glasses ⅞ inch square or circular, microscope lamp, lens paper.

PROCURING SUPPLIES FROM LOCAL SOURCES

The assistant should become thoroughly familiar with sources of help for his biology departmental program.

(1) Preserved human specimens may be secured from a hospital department of pathology. The assistant should become acquainted with the personnel of the pathology department and with the pathologists. These persons are in a position to be extremely helpful to a departmental program.

(2) Fresh materials such as sheep brains and beef joints may be obtained from local slaughterhouses or butchers. The assistant should develop the interest of butchers and slaughterhouse per-

sonnel. Excellent teaching materials can be procured from these sources.

(3) Solutions of various types and in various strengths may be obtained from a community pharmacist. It is often easier for the assistant to procure a solution made up by the pharmacist than to produce it himself in the department.

(4) Live animals such as rabbits may be secured from local rabbitries.

(5) Fertile eggs can generally be secured locally from persons who raise chickens.

(6) Various types of botanical and zoological specimens may be found locally in selected areas possessing an abundance of plant life and pond water.

(7) Local physicians, nurses, optometrists, and personnel in related biological science areas are good teaching resource personnel from whom to draw aid.

(8) Local hospital laboratories, health departments, and biological manufacturing companies are useful resources, and the personnel are generally eager to cooperate with biology departments toward a strengthened program.

BIOLOGICAL SUPPLY HOUSES

There are a number of companies that produce equipment, materials, supplies, and specimens used by biology departments. Various companies are specialists in particular offerings; some companies supply general needs. Each biology department has an arrangement for ordering supplies and conducting business with a particular company or companies.

The assistant should become familiar with the offerings of many different biological supply houses. Simply thumbing through a company catalog can provide the assistant with much new information regarding equipment, materials, and supplies of use in the biology program.

Departmental resources can be improved by placing on departmental shelves the catalogs of various companies. These catalogs generally contain interesting, concise, and helpful information regarding the general or trade name of the item, its quality, uses to which it can be put, cost in quantities for student use or as single units, pointers regarding its care, and special advantages to be derived from using the product. Familiarity with such broad information, gleaned from perusal of catalogs, can often be the stimulus for new ideas, suggestions and purchases of specimens and equipment that can add much strength to a department's offerings.

The assistant's ready familiarity with catalog literature can be a source of practical aid to the department head and permanent teaching staff within the department as plans are made for purchases. Various companies are constantly striving to improve their offerings, and the assistant should keep abreast of such improvements so that his department can benefit.

The assistant should learn the method of (1) requisitioning supplies for his department, (2) filling out and processing order forms, and (3) clearing orders with the department head and the institution's purchasing agent. Most of the mechanical details of handling and processing orders can be executed by the assistant so the department head and other teaching personnel can be free for more essential duties.

Supply Houses and Products

The following companies would likely supply a catalog of their products to the assistant upon his request:

American Optical Company (Buffalo, New York). Microscopes, optical equipment, microtomes.

Bausch and Lomb Optical Company (Rochester, New York), Microscopes and other optical equipment; microtomes.

California Botanical Materials Company, (787 Melville Avenue, Palo Alto, California). Microscope slides and preserved botanical materials; many Pacific coast species.

Cambosco Scientific Company (37 Antwerp Street, Brighten Station, Boston, Massachusetts). Biological materials, collecting supplies.

Carolina Biological Supply Company (Burlington, North Carolina). Living and preserved materials.

Central Scientific Company (1700 Boulevard, Chicago, Illinois). Laboratory apparatus.

Central Scientific Company (1702 Irving Park Road, Chicago, Illinois). General equipment.

Chicago Apparatus Company (1735-1743 North Ashland Avenue, Chicago, Illinois). General equipment.

Chicago Apparatus Company (1735 North Ashland Avenue, Chicago, Illinois). Biological materials, microscope slides, general laboratory apparatus, and reagents.

Difco Laboratories (920 Henry Street, Detroit 1, Michigan). Culture media and reagents.

Denoyer-Geppert Company (5235 Ravenswood Avenue, Chicago, Illinois). Preserved biological materials, microscope slides, charts, models, and general laboratory equipment.

Eastman Kodak Company (Rochester, New York). Projection apparatus; cameras; motion pictures; chemicals.

Edmund Scientific Company (99 East Gloucester Pike, Barrington, New Jersey). General equipment for the sciences.

Fisher Scientific Company (709-719 Forbes Street, Pittsburgh, Pennsylvania). Laboratory appliances and general equipment.

General Biological Supply House, (8200 South Hoyne Avenue, Chicago 20, Illinois). Living materials; microscope slides; general laboratory supplies.

Kewaunee Manufacturing Company (Kewaunee, Wisconsin). Laboratory furniture.

Keystone View Company (Meadville, Pennsylvania). Lantern slides.

Markle, M. S. (Earlham College, Earlham, Indiana). Preserved botanical materials; microscope slides.

Multiplex Display Fixture Company, (911-921 North Tenth Street, Saint Louis 1, Missouri). Display equipment.

New York Scientific Supply Company (30 West 30th Street, New York 1, New York). Preserved and living materials and microscope slides.

Oregon Biological Supply Company (1806 S.E. Holgate Boulevard, Portland, Oregon). Biological materials.

Powell Laboratories (Gladstone, Oregon. A subdivision of Carolina Biological Supply Company.) Living and preserved materials.

Powers and Powers, (Station A, Lincoln, Nebraska). Microscope slides of zoological materials.

Research Scientific Supplies, Division of Education Equipment Company (125 West 23rd Street, New York 11, New York.) General equipment.

Southern Biological Supply Company (517 Decatur Street, New Orleans, Louisiana). Living and preserved biological materials; microscope slides.

South Western Biological Supply Company (415 Tyler Avenue, Dallas, Texas). Living and preserved biological materials; microscope slides.

Stansi Scientific Company (1231 North Honore Street, Chicago 22, Illinois). General Equipment.

Tracerlab (1601 Tropelo Road, Waltham, Massachusetts). Radioactivity apparatus.

Triarch Botanical Products (Ripon, Wisconsin). Living and preserved botanical materials, microscope slides.

Triplett Electrical Instrument Company (500 Harmon Road, Bluffton, Ohio). Electrical instruments.

US Department of Agriculture (Washington, D.C.), Division of Motion Pictures. Supplies motion picture films; the Office of Cooperative Extension Work supplies lantern slides and film strips.

Vixter Animatograph Company (Davenport, Iowa). Projection apparatus.

Ward's Natural Science Establishment (302 Goodman Street, Rochester, New York). Preserved biological materials; microscope slides; skeletons; insect collections; fossils.

W. M. Welch Manufacturing Company (1516 Orleans Street, Chicago, Illinois). Preserved biological materials, microscope slides, and general laboratory equipment.

THE PROCUREMENT AND USE OF BIOLOGICAL MOTION PICTURES

Motion pictures are especially useful for visualizing various biological processes, especially through the use of time-lapse and slow-motion photography. There are hundreds of helpful films available at a small charge to the department or free of charge. Some films are in color. They are generally 16mm. productions with sound. Some are silent. Their running time is from 10 to 45 minutes.

The assistant should learn the names of various film suppliers and avail himself of their free catalogs with descriptions of various biological titles. His familiarity with these offerings can aid the department chairman and other members of the permanent teaching staff to locate a number of stimulating and informative films for visualizing vividly certain biological processes.

The following illustrative film descriptions, their titles and sources, will show the general nature of such available films.

Descriptions of Biological Films

The Amoeba. A 10-minute film available from United World Films, 1445 Park Avenue, New York 29, New York. Shows by microphotography and animated drawings the structure and life functions of living organisms, with pseudopodia, pursuit and capture of prey, ingestion, and reproduction by fission.

Budding Yeasts (Moniliasis). A 7-minute film, 1947, available from the Society of American Bacteriologists, University of Pennsylvania School of Medicine, Philadelphia, Pennsylvania. Time-lapse microphotography showing the process of reproduction of a pair of yeast cells.

Communicable Diseases. A 32-minute film available from CIBA Pharmaceutical Products, Summit, New Jersey. Patients with the following diseases are demonstrated: (1) reseola, (2) rubella, (3) measles, (4) chickenpox, (5) vaccinia, (6) herpes simplex, (7) zoster, (8) mumps, (9) scarlet fever, (10) staphylococcal abscess, (1) pertussis, (12) polio, (13) encephalitis, (14) meningitis, (15) acute tuberculosis, and (16) blastomycosis.

Skin Bank Storage of Postmortem Homografts (Methods of Preparation, Preservation, and Use). A 23-minute film available from the Surgical Film Library, American Cyanamid Company, 1 Casper Street, Danbury, Connecticut. Demonstrates how viable homografts from postmortem sources are used as biological dressings to save lives in severe burns. Details of the establishment of a skin bank and of the storage and use of the grafts are shown.

Effect of Serpasil (Reserpine) on Monkeys. A 15-minute film available from CIBA Pharmaceutical Products, Summit, New Jersey. A photographic laboratory report demonstrating the difference between the sedative action of two totally dissimilar drugs. Serpasil is shown to tranquilize and insulate the normal rhesus monkey against his environment to such an extent that he can be handled safely yet remains aware of his surroundings and is capable of a coordinated response to food and physical stimuli. On the other hand, the animal treated with a barbiturate is either brought to a state of anesthesia or, at a lower dose level, exhibits uncoordinated activity indicating detachment from his environment.

Enzyme Therapy with Varidase. An 18-minute film available from the Film Library, Lederle Laboratories, American Cyanamid Company, Pearl River, New York. The use of topical forms of Varidase Streptokinase-Streptodornase in treating various types of chronic ulcers, burns, peripheral vascular disease, infected maxillary sinuses, hemothorax, empyema, pilonidal cysts, and osteomyelitis. Patients are shown before, during, and after treatment with this nonsurgical method of debridement.

Escherichia Coli—Morphological Changes under the Influence of Antibacterial Substances. A 15-minute film available from CIBA Pharmaceutical Products, Summit, New Jersey. Shows the development of morphological changes in *Escherichia Coli* which can be observed under the influence of various antibiotics, disinfectants, and sulfonamides.

The Function of the Ear in Health and Disease. A 30-minute film available from Ayerst Medical Film Library, 321 West 44th Street, New York 36, New York. Based on an original research project, this demonstrates for the first time the physical action of the hearing mechanism in health and disease. Recordings of the motion of the normal and diseased ossicles reacting to music and speech are portrayed.

Improving the Hearing through Manipulation of the Middle Ear Structure. A 10-minute film available from the Film Library, Lederle Laboratories, American Cyanamid Company, Pearl River, New York. A brief review of the principles of hearing with an office procedure used to manipulate the middle ear structures. If mobility of the ossicular structure—namely, the malleus, incus, and stapes—is improved, hearing is improved. A special procedure, using a bougie through a catheter inserted in the Eustachian tube, is described and is shown being performed on an actual office patient, including demonstration of the preparation of the patient, the introduction of the Eustachian tube catheter so that medication and bougies will reach the nasopharyngeal orifice, and the precautionary measures taken. Describes the methods of selecting and using the proper nylon bougie. Using an especially adapted camera and lighting system, color motion pictures were taken through the drum membrane to allow the viewer to witness movement of the bougie and the manipulation of the inner ear structure.

The Inflammatory Reaction. A 26-minute film available from the Film Library, Lederle Laboratories, American Cyanamid Company, Pearl River, New York. Details the response of living tissue to trauma and injury. Points out that all inflammatory processes are the same regardless of cause. Uses microcinematography and animation. The causes of inflammation, normal body defense mechanisms with clinical cases, traumatic reactions at the cellular level, and the entire inflammatory process to tissue necrosis or the healing process are included.

Open Heart Surgery. A 27-minute film available from the Surgical Film Library, American Cyanamid Company, 1 Casper Street, Danbury, Connecticut. The physiologic hemodynamics related to defects in the interventricular septum are shown. Methods of closure utilizing extracorporeal bypass with a pump-oxygenator are included.

Pharmacology of Respiratory Stimulants. A 45-minute film available from CIBA Pharmaceutical Products, Summit, New Jersey. Shows the effect of Coramine on the respiratory, circulatory, and central nervous systems. Metabolism in the experimental animal. Several clinical uses of Coramine are shown.

Pudendal Block. This 25-minute film is available from Astra Pharmaceutical Products, Worcester 6, Massachusetts. The technique of pudendal block is demonstrated, anatomically, on a cadaver as well as on patients. A vaginal delivery is shown.

Use of the Artificial Kidney. A 15-minute film available from the Surgical Film Library, American Cyanamid Company, 1 Casper Street, Danbury, Connecticut. The film demonstrates the use of a mechanical cellophane apparatus to remove waste substances from the blood of patients with damaged kidneys.

Films such as these are available from a number of sources. The assistant should contact the following suppliers for further information regarding their film offerings.

Film Sources

Abbot Laboratories, North Chicago, Illinois.

American Heart Association, 257 West 57th Street, New York 10, New York.

Astra Pharmaceutical Products, Worcester 6, Massachusetts.

Ayerst Medical Film Library, 321 West 44th Street, New York 36, New York.

Bray Studio, 729 Seventh Avenue, New York 19, New York.

CIBA Pharmaceutical Products, Summit, New Jersey.

Encyclopedia Britannica Films, Inc., 1150 Wilmette Avenue, Wilmette, Illinois.

Erpi Picture Consultants, 250 West 57th Street, New York, New York.

International Film Bureau, 57 East Jackson Boulevard, Chicago 4, Illinois.

Medical Audiovisual Institute, 58 East South Water Street, Chicago 1, Illinois.

National Educational Television Film Service, Indiana University, Bloomington, Indiana.

Phase Films, 656 Austin Avenue, Sonoma, California.

Society of American Bacteriologists, University of Pennsylvania School of Medicine, Philadelphia, Pennsylvania.

Southern Illinois University, Carbondale, Illinois.

State University of Iowa, Bureau of Visual Instruction, Iowa City, Iowa.

The Film Library, Lederle Laboratories, American Cyanamid Company, Pearl River, New York.

The Surgical Film Library, American Cyanamid Company, 1 Casper Street, Danbury, Connecticut.

Upjohn Medical Films, The Upjohn Company, 7000 Portage Road, Kalamazoo, Michigan.

United World Films, 1445 Park Avenue, New York 29, New York.

U.S. Department of Health, Education and Welfare, Public Health Audiovisual Facility, Communicable Disease Center, Atlanta, Georgia 30333.

THE MICROTOME AND MICROTOME KNIFE

The microtome is a precision instrument and should be treated as such at all times. It should not be left exposed where it will accumulate dust and grime, which will get into the bearings and between sliding surfaces, increase the wear, and eventually produce inaccuracy. The microtome must be kept in its case or covered when not in use. It should not be lifted by any of its movable parts. After sectioning, the front of the microtome must be cleaned with a cloth moistened in xylol. Celloidin and freezing microtomes should be carefully dried. A fine oil, such as pike oil or paraffin oil, should be used for the sliding surfaces and for lubricating the bearings.

The microtome knife must be kept finely honed and stropped. Honing the knife consists of drawing the blade, cutting edge forward, diagonally over the face of the hone. The blade is then turned at the end of the stroke and drawn back, in the same manner and at the same oblique angle with reference to the hone, a number of times.

For stropping, there are two strokes. The first stroke on the coarser leather consists of drawing the knife heel forward diagonally across the strop, reversing and drawing it back again the same way, repeating the movement for thirty to fifty strokes. For the finishing stroke on the finely grained leather surface, the knife is pushed diagonally back and forth across the strop. Little pressure is required on the knife. It should merely lie flat on the strop or hone at the proper oblique angle, and be drawn or pushed, as the case may be, with little additional pressure.

For giving the cutting edge the proper bevel, a springback is usually provided for each blade. This should be clamped on the heel of the blade before honing and stropping.

The knife should be removed from the microtome immediately after use, wiped dry or cleaned with xylol, if necessary, and returned to its case.

THE KYMOGRAPH

The common form of this instrument consists of a revolving drum, powered by a spring in its base. The speed of the drum is easily controlled. The physiological activity such as muscle contraction is recorded on smoked paper placed around the drum. Data are secured and tracings are labeled on the smoked paper. The tracings are made permanent by passing the smoked page through a shellac bath after which it is allowed to dry.

The assistant should familiarize himself with the structure, purpose, and functional operation of the kymograph. He should learn the techniques of smoking the drum, and several blank tracings should be made. The inductorium, sources of current, and wire attachments for both single and tetanizing shocks should be studied. He may practice use of the instrument with a pithed frog.

After the paper has been smoked and placed on the drum, he should pith the animal. With stimulating electrodes connected to the inductorium, the various strengths of single and tetanizing shocks may be tested on the frog by fastening the frog to a frog board with clips, attaching a heart lever to one hind leg, and inserting a signal marker into the primary circuit of the inductorium and recording the results of the stimulations. The tracings may be fixed by treating them with the kymograph shellac fixing solution.

The assistant should consult various manuals with directions regarding detailed operation of the kymograph. He should practice using the instrument until he achieves proficiency.

THE PHYSIOGRAPH

The physiograph is a general purpose physiological recording instrument designed, developed, and built in the Laboratory of Biophysics of the Department of Physiology at Baylor University College of Medicine. Support for the development of this instrument came from the Heart Institute of the National Institutes of Health, a division of the United States Public Health Service. The instrument records a variety of physiological phenomena. With this instrument the assistant can aid the student to obtain directly inked records of any three physiological variables simultaneously. By proper selection of transducers, any group of three variables may be organized for simultaneous recording. For example, the pull of the auricle and ventricle of the heart of an experimental animal can be displayed simultaneously with the accompanying electrical signal. This record of the signal becomes an electrocardiogram. Thus, a single recording will present a comprehensive picture of many events of the cardiac cycle as they interrelate and vary with time.

The three basic components which constitute the physiograph system are the (1) transducer, (2) processor, and (3) reproducer. A combination of the three is called an information or data channel, or more simply, a channel. The transducer or pick-up converts the information to a signal which is more easily handled or processed than the original data. The processor then receives the transduced signal and operates on it. The operation may consist of amplification, attenuation, extraction of the square root or the logarithm or some other mathematical procedure to produce a signal acceptable to the reproducer. The reproducer or recording instrument is the device which converts the signal to a form suitable for reception by the human senses. A familiar example of this three-part system is the hi-fi phonograph. The pick-up is the transducer which converts the variations in the groove of the record to an electrical signal and passes it on to the amplifier. The processor is the amplifier which enlarges the signal to an intensity adequate to energize the loudspeaker. The loudspeaker is the reproducer which converts the electrical signal to sound waves for appreciation by the ears. The transducer is connected to the experimental animal or subject. In operation, its function may be to convert muscle pull, blood pressure, gut movement, respiration, air flow, or some other physiological event to a proportional electrical signal. This signal is then passed on to the amplifier which enlarges it. A control is provided on the amplifier to vary the degree of amplification. After enlargement, the signal is led to the recorder for reproduction.

One of the most useful reproducers in the physiology laboratory is the recording pen, because the maximum rate of change of many physiological quantities does not exceed the writing speed of high-quality direct recorders. Thus, using a direct inking pen, a graphic record is instantaneously available which describes the amplitude and time course of the physiological event. The physiograph consists of a group of measuring channels which permit the simultaneous written record of three physiological variables.

THE CARBON TETRACHLORIDE BOTTLE

A rather efficient killing bottle. Directions: Cut a small hole through the cork of the bottle and insert in this hole a small glass tube. Next, fasten a wad of cotton to the bottom of the cork and lower the tube so that it reaches the cotton at the bottom of the cork. The cotton may be saturated through the tube with carbon tetrachloride. This chemical is inexpensive. A small bottle of this killing agent may be carried along on field trips and added to the cotton at times through the small hole in the cork.

THE CHLOROFORM BOTTLE

Because of its capacity for absorbing chloroform, rubber is made use of in the chloroform bottle. Directions: Place a small handful of rubber bands in the bottom of a jar and cover them with chloroform. Let this stand overnight; then pour out all remaining chloroform and wedge a piece of cardboard over the bands. The rubber will have absorbed enough chloroform to keep the air in the bottle filled with fumes.

THE CYANIDE BOTTLE

Directions: Crush some sodium cyanide and place it in small lumps in the bottom of a jar with a wide mouth and a good stopper or tight lid. Put enough chopped cork, sawdust, or dry plaster of

Paris over the cyanide to level the surface. Pour about ½ inch of plaster of Paris over this and set it aside to dry. When dry, close the jar tightly and keep it closed except when in actual use. Cyanide is so deadly poisonous to all animals that it has to be handled with care. If a cyanide bottle cannot be purchased, a pharmacist will likely make one up. Each bottle should be clearly labeled "*Poison.*"

CARE OF EMBALMED CATS AND PIGS

When specimens show signs of drying out, the assistant should moisten them with the following carbo-glycerine solution, keeping them always in a cool place and protected from the air:

carbolic acid crystals	30 gm.
glycerine	250 cc.
water	1000 cc.

FORMALIN FUME CONTROL

The unpleasant odor of formalin (40% formaldehyde solution) can be relieved or prevented by adding a small quantity of a purchased formalin neutralizer solution to the stock container of formalin.

Irritating fumes from storage rooms and areas where formalin-preserved specimens are kept in loosely covered containers can be eliminated by the use of purchased formalin-fume inhibitors.

STERILIZING PETRI DISHES AND OTHER GLASSWARE

Directions: Wrap clean, dry Petri dishes in ordinary wrapping paper or paper sacks. Five or six Petri dishes may be placed in each package. Place the packages in a hot air sterilizer (a home kitchen oven is satisfactory) with a dry heat temperature of 160° to 170° C. (or 320° to 340° F.) for a period of two hours. Be careful to avoid heating over 180° C. (356° F.), as most paper chars at temperatures slightly higher than this. Allow the oven to cool slowly after the two-hour period. *Do not open the oven under any circumstances while it is hot.*

Chapter IV
Plants and Animals

PURPOSES

1. To emphasize the importance of general and specific laboratory and teaching techniques and methods which utilize plants and animals,

2. To provide for the assistant a series of specific steps of procedure for conducting a variety of professional techniques and methods,

3. To encourage the assistant to improve his professional efficiency through mastery of general and specific biological techniques and methods. The assistant will find that *Methods and Materials for Teaching Biological Sciences* (Miller and Blaydes) is an exceptionally comprehensive and authoritative volume of biological methods and procedures.

GRAFTING

All the better varieties of apples, pears, peaches, and plums can be reproduced by means of grafting and budding. The chief essential for success in grafting depends upon getting the cambium layers of the bud or stem that is to be grafted (cion) in contact with the cambium of the stem or root (the stock) on which it is to grow.

Materials. Stems: (about 1 inch in diameter and 1 foot long) of apple or pear; several twigs (3 to 4 inches long) with well-developed buds; cherry, plum, or peach stems (¼ to ½ inch in diameter and 8 to 10 inches long); twigs of the same with well-developed buds; growing tomato and potato plants; rubber bands; raffia; grafting wax or paraffin; sharp knife.

Grafting wax is made of 4 parts by weight of rosin, 1 part beeswax, and 1 part beef tallow. The whole mixture is melted by heating. The melted mass is poured into cold water. When cool enough to handle, it should be kneaded and pulled, as taffy is, or until it becomes a

139

creamy brown color. To apply to a graft it is pressed into crevices, covering all the cut surface.

CLEFT-GRAFTING

Directions: For cleft-grafting, select one of the large pieces of apple or pear stem as the stock. With a sharp knife split one of the ends. Select two twigs with buds as the cions, cut the stems into a wedge shape and insert the wedges in the split cleft of the stock so that the cambium layers of the stock and cion are in contact. With rubber bands or raffia (cotton string will do) wrap tightly the cleft end of the stock so as to hold the cions in place; cover the whole cut end, including the cleft portion, with grafting wax or paraffin to prevent drying out. The graft is then finished. If this can be done on a living tree and the growth watched, it makes a much finer demonstration.

THE IN-ARCH GRAFT

This graft may be made between a potato and tomato plant. Directions: Start the two in separate flower pots or together in a large pot. When the stems are 8 to 10 inches high, bring the stems into contact after slicing off enough tissue to expose a few vascular bundles of each stem at the point of contact. Carefully tie the stems together. Cover the wound region with paraffin or grafting wax. Allow growth to continue for three to four weeks, by which time union between the two stems is likely to have occurred. If so, the tomato stem between the graft union and the root may be severed. The upper part of the potato stem, above the union, may be removed. The tomato stem is now growing on the potato and gets its water and minerals through the potato roots. The lower part of the potato stem and its roots obtain food from the tomato leaves. With this graft it is possible to produce tomato fruits on the tomato parts of the plant and potato tubers in the soil.

STEM, LEAF, AND ROOT CUTTINGS

Many horticultural and wild plant species may be propagated from cuttings made from stems, roots, or leaves. With a little planning, the assistant can obtain sufficient demonstration material by assigning the work as a project for a group of students. A wooden box with sand, covered with a pane of glass, will serve as a growing site. Also, in many instances, a container for water (fruit jar) is sufficient. Some suggestions for plant forms to use are given below. Others, especially of local interest, will likely occur to the assistant or instructor. Many of the plants propagated may be used in other experiments as needs arise. Florists are excellent sources of aid with such matters as cuttings.

Materials: Stems of geranium, coleus, *Tradescantia* (wandering Jew), *Epiphyllum* (Christmas cactus,) *Opuntia* (prickly pear cactus), fushcia, German ivy (parlor ivy), English ivy, and rose. Roots of sweet potato, horse radish, *Paeonia*, blackberry, dewberry, sumac, sassafras, wisteria, and *Yucca* (Spanish bayonet). Leaves of *Rex begonia*, *Bryophyllum*, *Kalanchoe* (air plant), English ivy, *Peperomia*, rose, lilac and cabbage.

The stems of geranium, coleus, *Tradescantia*, German ivy, and English ivy may be rooted in a container of water, or in moist sand. Cuttings should not be over two to four inches long and should contain some of the more mature stem. If a damping-off fungus gets started, it is well to replace the sand and to wet the new sand with a solution of potassium permanganate (2 per cent solution in water). A temperature of about 65° to 70° F. is favorable for most cuttings. The fleshy roots of sweet potato may be sprouted by setting one end of the potato in a tumbler of water or burying in moist sand. From four to six weeks may be required for stem development.

The begonia leaves mentioned should have the thinner edges of the leaf removed and cuts made through the larger veins. Where the veins are cut a new plant may arise. The leaf is laid flat on moist sand. The leaves of English ivy, *Peperomia*, rose, lilac, cabbage, and sweet potato should have the petioles buried in the sand.

PREPARING SEEDLINGS AND PRODUCING PLANT GERMINATION

Directions: In order to grow bean seedlings about six inches tall, allow a three-to four-week growing period after planting the seeds. To produce germinating radish seeds with rootlets and root hairs, put seeds into a thoroughly moistened clay dish, cover lightly with wet filter paper, invert a beaker over the covered seeds, and allow about five to seven days growing time. Keep this arrangement moist throughout.

THE LABORATORY USE OF EXPERIMENTAL ANIMALS

Laboratory animals should receive humane treatment. The assistant must be sure that the cages are spacious, clean, and comfortable. Proper ventilation, correct temperature, adequate sunlight, continuous access to clean drinking water, and a well-balanced diet should be provided.

On a national scale there is a small but extremely vocal and active opposition to the use of animals for biological study. This opposition stems primarily from anti-vivisection societies, antiscientific healing cults, and perhaps well-intentioned but intellectually negative sources that supply the money for the opposition in the mistaken notion that cruelties are actually perpetrated in animal experimentation and that such studies are needless.

The assistant has an excellent opportunity to contribute to the solution of this antibiological attitude by assisting in a program of enlightened and continuous education with his students. The assistant should give serious thought to the entire philosophy of animal experimentation and perceive the rational justification for the humane sacrifice of lower animal life for important human advantage. Most animal experimentation is carried on simply because human life is held to be precious.

RULES GOVERNING USE OF LIVE ANIMALS

The assistant should observe a series of guiding principles in experimental work with live animals, as follows:

(1) Animals used for experimental purposes must be rendered unconscious by anesthesia or pithing;

(2) Only animals that are lawfully acquired may be studied in the laboratory, and their retention and experimental use must in every case be in compliance with the law;

(3) At the conclusion of experiments, the animals must be killed painlessly. Exception to this practice will be made in accordance with the opinion of the professor or laboratory director if continuance of the animal's life is necessary to determine the results of experiments. In such cases, the same aseptic precautions must be observed as when dealing with a human subject. Insofar as possible, care must be taken to minimize discomforts during the convalescence;

(4) When the use of live animals by students is essential for their biological education, the animals shall be used under the immediate supervision of the department head or director of laboratories.

BALANCING AN AQUARIUM

Balancing an aquarium means the establishment of the proper kinds and numbers of plants and animals in the correct amount of clean water under appropriate light and temperature conditions. In achieving the optimum state that exists in a balanced aquarium, difficulties are often encountered. In this connection, the following suggestions should be useful to the assistant:

(1) Obtain a clean aquarium tank. Test for leakage by filling the tank with water and permitting it to stand overnight.

(2) Place a layer of garden soil at least one-half inch deep in the tank. This should then be covered with a 1- to 2-inch layer of clean, washed sand. The sand should be shallow toward the front so that sediment and waste material may collect in this area and then be siphoned away.

(3) Add water slowly, pouring it carefully down the surface of a piece of clean paper or glass that is held obliquely in the tank. This will prevent stirring the sand. Clean pond water, spring water, or aerated tap water may be used. If chlorinated water must be used, it should be previously treated by boiling it vigorously, then letting it stand overnight, then pouring it back and forth to introduce air.

(4) Establish plants first. Place rooted plants such as *Vallisneria* and *Sagittaria* toward the back corners of the tank in the deeper sand. The plants must be placed deep enough that their roots are below the surface of the sand. Do not cover the leaves; this may kill the plants. Additional plants such as *Elodea*, *Cabomba*, *Myriophyllum* and *Ceratophyllum* may be placed toward the

center and front of the tank. Even these plants may not have roots when they are received, but they will eventually become rooted and so should be planted in the sand. If they tend to float free, they must be anchored in the sand by means of pebbles or small lead strips. Floating plants include *Lemna* (duckweed), *Azolla*, *Salvinia, Riccia flutans, Limnobium,* and *Pistia* (water lettuce). *Chara* and *Nitella* may either float free, or they may be anchored. All plants should be used sparingly. Too few plants are better than too many. Overstocking may cause all the plants to die.

(5) After two weeks, small fish, tadpoles, snails, and mussels should be added. Aquatic newts or small turtles may be introduced if a floating platform can be provided. Animals that are not compatible should be avoided. Do not use too many animals. *One inch of live fish to each gallon of water is a good rule.* Goldfish tend to destroy vegetation and so should be avoided.

(6) In securing a location for the aquarium, remember that a well-lighted place where sunshine is available at some time during the day is desirable. The latitude and the season of the year are important factors. In a northern latitude a southern exposure during winter months may be desirable; the same exposure during spring and summer will require some shading. When possible, light should be allowed to strike the aquarium from above. No more than two hours of direct sunlight should be permitted per day, especially during warm weather or if there is a tendency for the water to become warm. A glass plate covering for the aquarium will prevent evaporation and shield it against dust.

(7) The aquarium should be protected against sudden changes in temperature. The tank should be placed a short distance back from the window. It should not be placed near a radiator. A temperature range between 40° and 60° F. is ideal. A large tank of water will have a slower fluctuation of temperature than a small one.

(8) Since a newly established aquarium may lack sufficient food, a small amount of boiled lettuce leaves should be placed in the water for snails and tadpoles. The lettuce should be used sparingly and left for no more than a few hours, since decaying material will contaminate the water. Fish may be fed a small number of tiny worms, *Daphnia* (water fleas), or prepared fish food. Fish thrive well on very little food. Once the aquarium has become

established, little added food is needed. If soil is used under the sand, the plants should require very little extra food. If the plants fail to develop a healthy green color, a small amount of soluble food may be of value. Such food should be used sparingly until results become clear.

(9) Dead material should be removed promptly. A cloudy appearance may be produced by overstocking or by an unfavorable plant-animal ratio. An abundance of algae on the glass may be caused by too much light and may require shading with a green cloth. Excess algae should be scraped off with a razor blade and siphoned away. A balanced aquarium does not need running water.

(10) The most important factors are light, temperature, oxygen, and nutrients. Frequent observation and a sustained interest in the aquarium will help the assistant to profit from each day's experience and to achieve a final success.

THE TERRARIUM

The assistant will find this to be a most useful structure for laboratory activities. Many departments will not possess a terrarium, but the assistant can produce one himself with a good wooden box and cut glass. In most laboratories and green houses the humidity is so low that many plants cannot be grown successfully. However, with a terrarium high humidity can be maintained even in a very dry laboratory. The terrarium can be used for growing ferns, liverworts, some mosses, *Selaginellas*, and for starting seedlings and cuttings. A terrarium that contains a 2-to 3-inch layer of sifted pine duff (decayed litter from a pine forest) can be used quite successfully to grow fern prothallia and a number of other delicate plants. The terrarium can be used to demonstrate the typical plants of bog, swamp, woods, or desert. It is extremely useful for caging numerous small animals under nearly natural conditions.

TEMPORARY MOUNTS

The assistant should guide the student in carrying out the following steps of temporary slide preparation:

(1) See that his glass slide is thoroughly cleaned and dried.

(2) The student should place a small amount of the material to be

studied in the center of his slide. If it is not already wet enough, he should add a small drop of water.

(3) With such material as masses of fibers, he may tease the fiber out with two dissecting needles to ensure uniform distribution over the part of the slide that is to be covered with the cover glass.

(4) He should see that his cover glass is perfectly clean. Holding it by the edges between thumb and finger, or grasping one edge with the forceps, he should bring it into an oblique position against the material on the slide. As the cover glass drops from the oblique to the horizontal position, most of the air will be driven from underneath and will not interfere with his study of the material. With practice, he will learn how to control air bubbles and to prevent their occurrence.

(5) By means of a blotter or cloth, he should remove all excess water from around the edges of the cover glass, making sure that, except for the water film under the cover glass itself, both slide and cover glass are clean and dry.

(6) If, while he is examining a preparation, the water film under the cover glass shows a tendency to shrink by evaporation, he should use a dropper carefully to place a little additional water at the edge of the cover glass; the water will promptly pass as a thin film into the area covered by the cover glass.

FREEHAND SECTIONS

A section is a very thin slice of a plant part that is prepared in such a way as to permit microscopic study of its detailed structure.

Sections are most easily cut by holding the plant material between the thumb and forefinger. The side of the razor blade should be rested on the corner of the forefinger and the arms steadied by holding them close to the body.

Slices are made with a long stroke toward the body. A number of sections should be cut and the thinnest selected for study. The sections should be floated off the razor blade into a watch glass or Petri dish of water.

LABELING SLIDES

Directions: Prepare a very dilute solution of balsam, using xylene for dilution. With this solution, paint the end of the slide to be labeled. Allow it to dry slightly. Write directly in the undried balsam with India Ink. Another coat of balsam may be given after the ink dries. The balsam should be diluted enough to dry within a few minutes after application. Purchased glass-marking pens may also be used for labeling slides.

MACERATION OF TISSUES

(1) Longitudinal pieces of roots or stems are cut into pieces about 1 mm. in thickness. These are dropped into a solution of equal parts of 10 percent chromic acid and 10 percent nitric acid (Jeffrey's maceration solution). The solution must be used immediately after it is made.

(2) Let the material stand in the solution for 24 to 48 hours and examine. If it falls apart by teasing with a dissecting needle, it is ready to be removed.

(3) Filter with filter paper in a funnel.

(4) Wash the material thoroughly with tap water by running the water into the filter until no sign of the acid remains. The residue may be stored in 50 or 70 percent alcohol until needed for mounting.

(5) The residue is made up of tissue elements. It is excellent material for studying cell forms. A small amount may be mounted in glycerin and studied immediately as temporary preparation mounts. Or it may be stained and mounted permanently.

(6) Staining is done in the filter the same as washing. Dehydration is also accomplished by pouring alcohol over the residue in the filter. Clearing with xylene may be done in the same way, or the residue may be transferred to a small dish of xylene. With a dry camel's hair brush, small bits of the material may be transferred to balsam on a slide. Covering and drying are then done as usual.

EXPERIMENTS IN FEEDING PROTOZOA

After clearing *Amoeba* and *Chaos* of food, the assistant should add any of the following one hour before meeting the laboratory students: *Blepharisma*, *Paramecium bursaria*, and *Stentor coeruleus* (to *Chaos* only). Upon observation, *Amoeba* should contain numerous particles and usually living protozoans, thereby producing a beautiful color contrast for student viewing.

If the culture does not contain sufficient *Paramecium* and *Chilomonas* are not too plentiful, add one grain of rice. When cultures appear too rich in food and *Chilomonas*, remove food. To concentrate paramecia, place a light bulb close to one side of the culture jar. Paramecia will group on the opposite side.

The feeding method for *Didinium nasutum*, *Pelomyxa carolinensis*, and *Bursaria truncatella* requires excellent cultures of *Paramecium caudatum*. By means of a dropping pipette, the paramecia are removed in large numbers without getting too much medium. Place the organisms in fresh spring water in culture dishes. Strain through several thicknesses of fine cheesecloth. This will remove the debris and large masses of bacteria. Allow to stand until the paramecia congregate in white masses on the bottom of the dishes; the animals may then be removed in quantity with a dropping pipette and added to spring water in other dishes. *Didinium*, *Pelomyxa*, or *Bursaria truncatella* may be inoculated into these. Since all three organisms are voracious feeders on paramecium, more of the latter must be added every few days. Subcultures should be prepared about every two weeks.

PRODUCING CONJUGATION IN PARAMECIUM BURSARIA

1. Examine a drop of the medium from each of two cultures received. Individual paramecia will be found, but no conjugation pairs.

2. Using separate dropping pipettes in a deep-well culture slide, mix some culture medium containing paramecia from each of the two cultures. This may be done by the assistant as a demonstration or by each student as a part of the regular laboratory work after demonstration by the assistant.

3. Examine the organisms under the binocular dissecting microscope. Agglutination may be observed almost immediately.

4. Place the well-slide on a piece of moistened blotter paper and cover it with a finger bowl to prevent excessive evaporation of the culture medium.

5. Examine again after several hours. Conjugating paramecia should begin to appear. The number of conjugating pairs will increase gradually.

6. Examine the culture again after 24 hours. Many conjugating paramecia should be observed. Some conjugants may be observed in the act of separation.

7. Examine again after 48 hours have elapsed. Few or no conjugants will then be observed.

THE FROG IN LIVE EXPERIMENTS

Many of the experiments in the laboratory make use of the frog as an experimental animal. The frog is used because it is a cold-blooded animal and the tissue need not be kept at a rigidly controlled temperature. Because the frog carries on cutaneous as well as pulmonary and buccopharyngeal respiration, the thorax and abdomen can be opened without interrupting respiration.

PITHING A FROG

The assistant should practice this technique on an etherized or dead frog until skill is attained. Extend the legs of the frog and wrap the animal in a moist paper towel. Hold the frog, with its head up, in the left hand, being careful not to squeeze. Place the left index finger over the front of the head and bend the head forward to separate the occipitovertebral junction. Find this junction depression with the right index finger. Push the needle point into the depression and move it quickly from side to side. This movement cuts across the medulla. Then turn the needle forward into the cranial cavity, and move the needle around to destroy the brain. To destroy the spinal cord, turn the needle downward into the spinal cavity and move it about several times.

PREPARING A SPINAL FROG

To prepare a spinal frog, use a normal animal. A spinal organism is one in which the entire brain is destroyed, while the spinal cord is left intact. With the right hand, pick up the animal by its hind legs and hold it tightly. Then place the frog dorsal side up into the palm of the left hand and clamp the head between the left index finger and middle finger. Hold the left thumb firmly over the animal's trunk. Next, release the hind legs and pick up a pithing needle with the free hand. Draw the needle point lightly along the middorsal line of the frog's anterior region. At the point of union of head with trunk, a middorsal depression can be felt. This is the juncture of skull and vertebral column. Plunge the needle point vertically into this depression until the bone penetration has been felt and the spinal cord has been pierced. Now move the handle of the needle from side to side to sever the spinal cord. While leaving the needle in the puncture, and holding it exactly in line with the longitudinal axis of the frog, lower the handle toward the animal's back so that the needle points forward, bend the head of the frog slightly down with the holding fingers, and push the needle point into the brain. If the technique is properly executed, no bony obstruction will be encountered, and the needle will penetrate as far as the anterior end of the brain case. Then the needle handle should be moved from side to side to destroy the brain. The needle should then be withdrawn. The spinal frog should then be placed into its finger bowl. It should be left undisturbed for at least ½ hour to allow recovery from the shock of the operation.

PREPARING A DECEREBRATED FROG

To prepare a decerebrated frog, use an anesthetized animal. A decerebrated organism is one in which the cerebrum, but no other part of the brain or spinal cord, has been destroyed. Put the animal into a dissecting tray with the dorsal side up. Find the brown, circular tympanic membrane on each side, behind the eyes. Draw an imaginary line from the anterior margin of one eardrum to the anterior margin of the other eardrum. Place a razor blade or a very sharp scalpel along this imaginary line and cut vertically downward until the whole anterior part of the skull is severed away. Leave the lower jaw intact. This technique removes all of the brain anterior to the optic lobes; that is, it removes the forebrain, including the cerebral hemispheres. Place the decerebrated frog into a finger bowl containing fresh water. Leave it there for at least ½ hour, during which time the anesthesia and the shock of the operation will wear off.

INDUCING OVULATION IN FROGS

Large female frogs should be used. They should be obtained fresh from hibernation. From the January to May period they may be kept at 4° C. in the laboratory refrigerator. Animals that are used for induced ovulation should not be reared or stored at room temperature because the eggs will deteriorate.

To induce ovulation, frog pituitary glands are injected into the abdominal cavity two days before the eggs are desired, according to the following schedule of dosage:

September to January .... 10 male or 5 female glands
February .... 8 male or 3 female glands
March .... 5 male or 3 female glands
April .... 4 male or 2 female glands

One ovulating female will supply enough eggs for a large class. Mammalian pituitary extracts should not be used for inducing ovulation in frogs. Comprehensive directions for induction procedure may be found in *Experimental Embryology*, by Roberts Rugh (Burgess Publishing Co., Minneapolis, 1948).

COLLECTING AQUATIC FORMS FROM PONDS, POOLS, AND STREAMS

In capturing actively swimming insects, such as the whiligigs (Gyrinidae and water striders (Gerridae), a dip net is advisable. Its straight edge is useful for dredging bottoms. When these surface forms are to be kept alive, they may be kept in vessels of the water or placed in wet grass or sphagnum moss until they reach the laboratory. They must be closely caged or they will escape in transit. When placed in an aquarium they must be covered with glass or a screen to prevent their escape.

COLLECTING SUBSURFACE FORMS

Diving beetles (Dytiscidae), back swimmers (Notonectidae), and giant water bugs (Belostomatidae) may be found beneath the surface at various depths; these amimals always come to the surface at intervals for air. These may be captured by the dip net and returned to the laboratory in the same manner as the surface forms.

PRESERVING INSECTS

The almost universal method of preserving the insect is that of thrusting a pin through the body after it has been killed but before it has dried. By the time the insect has dried thoroughly it has become firmly fastened to the pin.

The usual method of pinning the insect is to place the pin through the thorax. In the case of beetles, however, the pin is thrust through the right wing cover. Very small insects that cannot be pinned are usually mounted with glue on a heavy paper "point." These should be laid on their side unless two specimens are available. When two are available, they may be mounted by gluing one dorsal side up and the other ventral side up.

COLLECTION BOXES

A heavy cardboard box such as a candy box can be used, and cigar boxes, especially the better grade of box, are convenient.

The best way to prepare the collection box is to place a layer of sheet cork on the bottom and glue over it a layer of white paper. Sheet cork may be secured as scraps and cuttings at furniture stores or as pads for hot dishes at five-and-ten-cent stores. When pins are thrust into it, they stay firmly set and stand upright. If cork cannot be obtained, however, a sheet of heavy corrugated box may serve as a substitute. Heavy, loose fiber wallboard also does very well for collection box purposes.

PINNING INSECTS

When a box has been filled with insects, all the insects on paper points should be at the same height. The height must be regulated at the time of pinning, since it is not possible to change the height after the insect dries.

MOUNTING INSECTS

Large forms such as moths and butterflies can best be kept in good condition by placing them in Ricker mounts, which are cardboard boxes with glass tops. The box is filled with cotton, which holds the insect in place and makes a contrasting background.

Ricker mounts are expensive. A good substitute can be made by taking narrow strips of wood and constructing a frame, tacking or gluing a heavy cardboard back on the frame, and placing a glass plate over the top. The glass should be fastened around the edge with glued tape.

The other method of mounting for display consists in cutting frames from heavy cardboard. These may be made any desired size. To increase the thickness, several layers of cardboard are used. Sheet cellophane is glued over one side of the frame. The insect is placed inside the frame and stuck to the cellophane with glue or cement (cellophane cement can be purchased), and the other side of the frame closed with another sheet of cellophane. When mounted in this manner the specimen may be viewed from either side. Very small forms may be placed in thin frames and examined under the microscope. The materials are inexpensive and the mounts will last a long time.

BROWNIAN MOVEMENT

Molecules are too small to be seen except with the highest-powered microscope, but impacts of such moving molecules with small, but visible, particles of other substances may cause the visible particles to move, and this movement may be detected under magnification. The peculiar vibrating movement of these tiny visible particles is known as "Brownian movement."

Materials: compound microscope with a high-power objective (4mm.); microscope slide and cover glass; water; and a small quantity of some finely divided substance that is not soluble in water (chalk dust, wall plaster, air-slaked lime, or lampblack).

Directions: Place a tiny bit of the chalk dust or other selected substance upon the microscope slide in a drop of water. Cover with a cover glass. Examine with a high-power objective.

Look for vibratory motion of the small visible particles in the water. They do not move across the field of view from one side to the other; they move back and forth in random paths.

DIFFUSION MEMBRANES

In preparation of diffusion membranes, goldbeater's skin or porous-type cellophane may be used. Directions: The skin or cellophane should be cut to required size, wet with water, and put over the end of a glass tube. Use an uncut rubber band to hold while pulling membrane in place. Avoid pleats. Wind a cut, stretched rubber band securely around the tube, near its end. Tie. Test for leakage by placing in water and blowing into the tube.

THE ACETOCARMINE METHOD FOR CHROMOSOMES

The acetocarmine method, often known as the "smear" method, permits observation of chromosomes within five minutes after they are taken from living tissues. The stages of mitosis or meiosis can be demonstrated, and the chromosomes can be counted. The method is applicable chiefly to the sporogenous tissue of anthers and microsporophylls of such conifers as pine and juniper. Lily anthers are excellent for such studies. If these are not available, any flower that is obtainable may be tried. In winter, pine branches brought into the laboratory and placed in water for several days may produce staminate cones, a series of which may show all stages of mitosis and the reduction division of meiosis. Anthers of cones preserved in acetic alcohol are also highly satisfactory. Buds approximately one-fourth grown are usually in about the right state for such work.

Directions: With a needle, crush a small piece of the microsporophyll in a drop of acetocarmine on a clean slide. Remove the debris with forceps. Cover with a cover glass. Warm over a flame for about one second four or five times. The slide is now ready for examination. If it is overstained, add a drop of acetic acid under the cover glass and heat, then observe.

THE GRAM STAIN

Directions:

(1) Thoroughly clean a cover glass with ether or by scouring with pumice stone.
(2) Place a loop of water on the clean cover glass.
(3) Touch a pure culture of the bacteria with the sterile needle; touch the drop of water but do not agitate.
(4) Pass the needle through a flame several times to sterilize it. After cooling, spread the culture drop by means of the side of the sterilized needle.
(5) Allow the film to air-dry.

(6) Holding the cover glass with forceps, fix the bacteria by passing it through flame three times at 1-second intervals.

(7) Stain 3 to 4 minutes with Gram's aniline gentian violet.

(8) Rinse by carefully flowing water over the cover glass. Stain in Lugol's iodine for 1 minute.

(9) Rinse with 95 percent alcohol until the excess stain is removed.

(10) Rinse with water, and stain with 1 percent safranin for about 1 minute.

(11) Rinse with water and allow to become air-dry. Dehydrate by passing through 100 percent alcohol. Air-dry the smear; invert the cover glass in a drop of balsam on a slide. Some bacteria stain blue (gram positive), while others lose the blue and stain red in the safranin (gram negative). This method is used often to differentiate between organisms.

MUCOSAL SCRAPING

In scraping, use is made of the scalpel. Directions: Hold stomach or intestine over finger. Scrape a small area of organ surface. Use the blade surface of the scalpel at the tip. Place a drop of saline on a clean slide. Use a dissecting needle to scrape the material into solution. Use two dissecting needles to separate the material well. Place the cover slip. Look for small areas of tissue. Look for edges rather than surfaces, and torn edges rather than cut edges.

ADMINISTERING CHLOROFORM OR ETHER

Directions: For small animals, a crushed paper towel is placed in a large battery jar. Pour in a little ether. Cover the jar with paper towel and glass plate. Raise the lid and put the animals in, then re-cover the jar. Hold the lid down for a few minutes.

For a larger animal use a bell jar. Put the animal under the jar and introduce the chloroform or ether on cotton or on a paper towel.

ADMINISTERING URETHAN

The necessary dose of a 10 percent solution is 3 mg. of urethan per gram of frog body weight, injected into the ventral lymph sac. To inject, wrap the frog in a moist paper towel and hold the animal in the left hand. Put the needle of a hypodermic syringe into the angle of the mouth, inserted so that it will be just under the skin. Turn the needle downward, then toward the midventral line into the ventral lymph sac.

ADMINISTERING NEMBUTAL

Directions: Prepare a solution that will contain 35 mg. of drug per 3 ml. of water. The necessary dose is 35 mg. per kilogram of body weight, given intraperitoneally. When using this stock solution, if the required dose for a small animal is less than 1 ml., add water to make 1 ml.

Dosage Example:

Rat weight is 65 gm.

$35:1000 = x:65$

$1000x = 2275$

$x = 2.275$ mg.

There are 35 mg. in 3 ml. or 45 minims of water. So to give 2.275 mg.,

$35:45 = 2.275:x$

$35x = 102.4$

$x = 2.9$ or 3 minims

Pull up 3 minims of the stock solution into a hypodermic syringe and then sufficient water to make 15 minims or 1 ml. While dealing with the animal directly, it should be held gently by fore and hind legs.

EMBALMING

Larger Animals. When an animal larger than a rat or guinea pig is to be preserved, especially if it is to be used for careful dissection, it is best used in the embalmed state. The assistant will find details for embalming animals such as a cat or dog in a number of books (or by referring to Turtox Service Leaflet number 21 described in Chapter II).

In order to conduct the embalming procedure, the assistant will need dissecting scissors, scapel, sharp knife, forceps, injecting syringe, needles, thread, embalming fluid, ether, chloroform or jet of gas, and a spreading board.

INJECTING

The study of the circulatory system is much easier if injected animals are used. Latex, which can be purchased from a biological supply house, is the most satisfactory injecting medium. It comes as a liquid, colored medium that is ready for use. It solidifies upon injection.

The animal should be killed just prior to the injection in order to prevent clotting. The injection needle should be placed either (1) in the carotid artery of the neck pointing toward the heart, (2) in the aorta, or (3) in the femoral artery. The needle should be tied into the vessel with a thread, which is then drawn tight when the needle is removed to prevent the latex from leaking.

Pressure should be applied very gently during the injection in order to prevent rupturing the vessels. If a vessel is ruptured it is impossible to inject the vessels beyond the break. The gums or the undersurface of the tongue and eyelids will show definite color changes when the injection has reached the capillaries successfully. The veins can be injected from the femoral, jugular, or hepatic portal.

FIXING KYMOGRAPH PAPER

An oblong container is needed, size about 9½ x 5 x 2½ inches, plus an enamel tray or piece of glass for cover. The paper is held carefully by each end with the record side up. The paper is introduced into the fluid, then pulled back and forth until covered. It is then drained by hanging over newspaper.

FORMALIN AS FIXATIVE AND PRESERVATIVE

A 5 percent formalin solution (95 cc. distilled water and 5 cc. stock formaldehyde) is used for killing and fixing the following forms: flukes, *Microstomum*, *Ascaris*, Bryozoa, *Lumbricus*, frog larvae and eggs, salamanders, and salamander larvae.

A 5 percent formalin solution is used for preserving the following forms: *Epistylis*, *Opercularia*, planaria, flukes, *Microstomum*, *Ascaris*, oligochaetes, leeches, grass frogs, frog eggs and larvae, salamanders, and salamander larvae.

A 10 percent formalin solution (90 cc. distilled water and 10 cc. stock formaldehyde) is used for killing and fixing the following forms: Obelia, anemones, Campanularia, Gonothyrea, Syncoryne, Tubularia, Actinozoa, Pleurobrachia, starfish, sea cucumber, tapeworms, rotifers, oligochaetes, leeches, Daphnia, crayfish, slugs, snails, clams, Dolichoglossus, Salpa, Cynthia, lampreys, fish and reptiles.

A 10 percent solution is used as a preservative for the following forms: Obelia, anemones, Campanularia, Gonothyrea, Syncoryne, Tubularia, Actinozoa, Pleurobrachia, starfish, sea cucumber, tapeworms, Daphnia, crayfish, slugs, clams, Dolichoglossus, Salpa, Cynthia, lampreys, fish, reptiles, rabbits, guinea pigs, rats, mice, and large animals.

ESTABLISHING A RAT COLONY

In some college localities, rats may be purchased from local dealers; it is much better, however, to maintain a colony on the campus for laboratory use. The assistant will find that D'Amour and Blood's Manual for Laboratory Work in Mammalian Physiology is perhaps the outstanding volume dealing with the rat in laboratory investigations.

The colony should be begun with good stock. Rats from Philadelphia's Wistar Institute are excellent. The best of the progeny should be selected for use as breeders. If work is to begin in the fall, the colony should be organized in the spring. At six months of age rats will have reached their full size. Litters run from six to eight.

The colony should be housed in a room which can be kept warm; a temperature range of from 70° to 80° F. is satisfactory. This room need not be large; two large cages for the adults and about a dozen small ones for mothers and babies will prove sufficient for general purposes. Purina chow or a similar feed, supplemented twice a week with lettuce and carrots, serves as a satisfactory diet. The water dishes must be washed daily. Wood shavings are satisfactory for bedding. The cages must be cleaned weekly. Spraying the cages lightly with a 5 percent DDT solution once each month and scouring with soap and hot water every three months will control insects and prevent odors.

Males and females may occupy the same cage. The females should be removed when they become obviously pregnant. If controlled breeding is desired, the sexes may be kept separated and the females observed for estrus. Estrus recurs every 4 to 5 days. It is marked by reddening and swelling of the vaginal orifice. If females in estrus are placed with males overnight, breeding will almost invariably occur. The period of gestation is 21 to 22 days. Shortly before parturition the females should be put into individual cages and supplied with excelsior for nest-building. The babies should be weaned after three weeks. The mothers should then be given a rest period of a few weeks before being mated again.

HANDLING RATS

Rats that are not accustomed to being handled may bite, but rats cannot bite with their mouths shut. Therefore, a rat should be held with the thumb and index finger around and below the lower jaw. It should not be held around the throat. Do not squeeze the body or throat. Squeezing causes the rat to struggle for escape. A rat may be easily picked up by the tail. This does it no harm. It will simply pull away and can be picked up while straining. A rat cannot be held long suspended by its tail, however, because it will climb up and bite. Gloves may be worn, but these are inconvenient and unnecessary if proper technique is used.

The assistant and students who are unaccustomed to handling rats may well spend some time merely picking them up and transferring them from one box to another, until the general "feel" of the rat and its reactions to stimuli have been thoroughly experienced and confidence is gained in the ability to control the animal.

WEIGHING RATS

A spring balance is satisfactory. Rats will usually try to jump off the pan and escape; the rat should be put into a paper bag while weighing; later the weight of the bag should be subtracted.

INJECTION METHODS FOR RATS

Substances in solution are frequently administered in physiological work. Three general methods are used: (1) subcutaneous, (2) intraperitoneal, and (3) oral. For oral administration, it is not necessary to have the material at body temperature. It should, however, be warmed.

Subcutaneous Injection

This type of injection work is done with the animal on a table. Directions: Grasp the rat firmly with the left hand, with one finger enclosing the lower jaw. Avoid holding the throat. Pinch up the skin of the back between the thumb and the index finger. Holding the syringe in the right hand and pointing it toward the head, insert the needle with a quick thrust and inject the solution. Withdraw the needle and massage the site of injection to prevent escape of the fluid.

If the assistant prefers, towels can be placed over the rats to aid in holding them while injections are made. The towels should be placed over the head and forefeet and the animal held firmly.

Intraperitoneal Injection

Directions: The rat should be held in the left hand with the thumb around the lower jaw. The throat should be avoided. The animal should be pressed against the left side of the body. This will hold the animal securely and will stretch the skin across the abdomen. The injection should be made in the lower middle of the abdomen with a quick thrust. A short ½-inch, 24- to 26-gauge needle should be used.

ORAL ADMINISTRATION WITH RATS

Oral administration of liquid material should be made with a large-guage, bent syringe needle that is equipped with a ball tip.

Directions: The rat should be held in the left hand, with the sides of the head between the thumb and index finger and the animal braced against the assistant's left side. The syringe and needle should be filled previously with the desired amount of material. The ball tip is then inserted into the animal's mouth and very gently pushed downward. The tip will slide easily into the esophagus and should then be pushed onward into the stomach. If any obstruction is felt, no force should be exerted, but another effort should be made to find the esophageal opening.

The assistant should practice injecting at first into lightly anesthetized rats until the technique is mastered, then he can repeat the technique on conscious rats. He should also practice controlling the volume injected, that is, injecting 0.25 cc., 0.50 cc., and so on, from a full syringe. Sterile saline warmed to 30° or 35° C. should be used in such practice injections.

ANESTHETIZING RATS

As a basal anesthetic, nembutal (sodium pentobarbital) is very satisfactory. The dose used is 50 mg. per kilogram for males, 40 mg. for females, injected subcutaneously. Anesthesia will be complete in 20 to 30 minutes and will last about one hour; if the operation is prolonged, a further dose of 20 mg. per kilogram may then be given. If necessary, the nembutal may be supplemented with small amounts of ether during the course of the operation.

For operations of short duration, ether alone may be used. A pad of cotton is sprinkled with ether and placed in a large jar, the cotton is covered with a folded paper towel, the rat is then placed carefully in the jar, and the jar covered securely.

When the rat collapses, he should be removed, and etherization continued from a Gooch crucible containing a cotton pad moistened with ether. From time to time the ether must be renewed by dipping the Gooch crucible into an evaporating dish containing ether.

The assistant should practice anesthetizing rats and observing the progress of the depth of anesthesia by pinching the ears or tail. The respiratory movements are also a good index to the depth of anesthesia. When breathing is slow and shallow, too much ether is being given; when breathing is rapid and deep, too little.

RESUSCITATION OF RATS

For the sake of practice, overdoses of ether should purposely be given and the assistant should attempt resuscitation. Emergencies will invariably occur occasionally during the course of anesthetization, and there will be cases in which resuscitation is needed. The assistant should always be prepared for such eventualities.

Have available a soft rubber tube with a bore large enough to fit over the rat's nose, with a glass tube attached. When respiration ceases, the rubber tube should be pressed against the rat's nose. Air should be gently blown and sucked from the lungs at a rate of about 30 times per minute, with periodic pauses to determine whether the rat has resumed breathing. If too long a time has not elapsed, respiration can almost always be restored by this means.

IDENTIFYING RATS

Individual rats can be marked for identification by rubbing methylene blue solution into the hair on the back of their heads or various other parts of their bodies.

THE CARE OF CHAMELEONS AND TURTLES

Chameleons and turtles should be kept in a terrarium or in an empty aquarium tank to which a small amount of grass or straw has been added. The container should be covered with a wire screen. In the case of turtles, about ¼ inch of water should be added. Both turtles and chameleons will feed on mealworms (about 7 to 8 worms per animal every 10 days.) Water should be placed in the tank with chameleons.

Chapter V
Biological Cultures

PURPOSES

1. To provide for the assistant a number of general and specific sources and methods of preparation of various types of biological cultures,

2. To outline special precautions for caring for biological cultures in the department and in the laboratory,

3. To equip the assistant for maintaining biological cultures as a means of guaranteeing anticipated results in departmental and laboratory activities,

4. To encourage the assistant to master a series of techniques that strengthen the proficiency of the professional biologist.

BIOLOGICAL CULTURES

The assistant is generally responsible for maintaining cultures of various animal and plant forms during the normal course of departmental operations. There are a number of culture media and techniques available, and organisms require varying types of specialized treatment. The assistant should learn and apply the specific requirements for maintaining satisfactory cultures for a number of forms. The information in the sections that follow is designed to prepare him to handle those organisms generally utilized in a typical biology departmental program of studies.

ALGAE

The following points are of special importance in the cultivation of algae:

(1) The total amount of light required daily varies with the species.

(2) Excessive light may damage algae by its heating effect.

(3) A temperature around 70° F. is optional for a number of species of algae.

(4) The optimal pH of different species varies widely. A reaction somewhere near neutral probably is best where precise control over a large number of species is not feasible.

(5) The organic content of media varies widely.

(6) Oxygenation of cultures by bubbling air through them may be of doubtful value.

GENERAL CULTURE MEDIA AND METHODS FOR VARIOUS MICROORGANISMS

The successful culture of any microorganism depends on the choice of a suitable culture medium and proper care and handling. This involves a careful consideration of the factors that influence the growth of the organism and its reproduction. These factors must be favorable if cultures are expected to develop. Care must be exercised in choosing the water and the ingredients used in the culture media, in methods of preparation, and in selecting proper food organisms. Optimal temperature, pH, and light conditions must be maintained. Contamination must be avoided. Periodic renewal of the cultures must be secured by proper subcultivation.

In their natural habitats, organisms live under a wide variety of conditions. They flourish in one situation; they barely maintain themselves in another. Therefore, when cultivated in the laboratory under much more uniform conditions, most species will give difficulty sooner or later. Periods of depression may occur in spite of all measures that are taken to prevent them. The causes may be entirely unrelated in various instances.

In all culture work the assistant should keep the following points in mind:

(1) Choose a water that has no toxic properties. Tap water from the laboratory is generally unsuitable for culture work.

(2) Pasteurize all media and allow to cool to room temperature before innoculating. Sterilize all bacteriological media.

(3) Keep cultures covered in order to exclude dust but not air.

(4) Prepare subcultures only at the time that the parent cultures have reached maximum populations. Use boiled or sterilized dropping pipettes and inoculate heavily.

(5) Culture vessels must always be clean. Traces of chemicals, soap, or soap powders may be extremely toxic to organisms.

(6) Keep each dropping pipette and the culture for which it is intended together. Do not use these interchangeably.

(7) Wash hands thoroughly with soap and hot water before beginning any culture work with bacteria and fungi.

(8) While working in the laboratory, minimize all air movements by closing windows and turning off electric fans.

(9) Wipe the work tables with 70 percent alcohol before beginning culture work or transferring bacteria and fungi.

(10) Sterilize all needles and loops over a flame before and after using. To prevent any scattering of pathogenic material stuck to the loop, dip it in phenol solution before flaming.

(11) Autoclave all glassware at 15 pounds pressure for 15 minutes or sterilize by dry heat at 160° C. for 2 or more hours.

(12) Clean all glassware with cleaning fluid or a detergent such as trisodium phosphate and thoroughly rinse it.

(13) If possible, use only Pyrex or other heat- and chemical-resistant glassware.

(14) Do not place cultures in direct sunlight or into an extremely hot or cold environment.

(15) Sterilize immediately all cultures infected with such undesired laboratory "weeds" as *Rhizopus, Penicillium,* and *Aspergillus.*

(16) Strict sanitation and occasional fumigations with carbon tetrachloride help to reduce mite populations in culture cabinets.

(17) Since the available food supply (depending on the temperature) is exhausted within a few days, cultures reach their maximum development in that period of time. The organisms then begin to die or to produce spores slowly at first, and then more rapidly. In order to maintain thriving cultures, it is necessary to transplant some of the organisms to a fresh medium. At ordinary room temperatures this transfer may be made weekly or every 2 weeks. A good practice is to set up new cultures from 24 to 48 hours before they will be needed.

(18) Pathogenic organisms must be handled with extreme care in order to avoid infections. Remember that these organisms, even though not growing at the expense of living tissues, are nevertheless capable of causing disease. The contents of such cultures should not be poured down laboratory sinks or discarded in waste cans. They should be destroyed by autoclaving, by strong disinfectants, by boiling thoroughly for 1 hour, or by burning.

BACTERIA AND FUNGI

A great variety of liquid and solid media are available for the cultivation of bacteria and fungi. For information regarding special media, the assistant may consult textbooks or the periodical literature on bacteriology and mycology.

In general, the media are all solidified through the inclusion of agar. They may be poured into Petri dishes as plates or dispensed into culture tubes as slants. Most of them may be purchased in dehydrated form. If prepared from separate ingredients, the pH in all except Sabouraud's agar should be brought to 7.-7.4 by the addition of a small quantity of a normal solution of sodium hydroxide. All media should be sterilized in the autoclave at 15 pounds pressure for 15 minutes.

BACTERIAL GRASS-INFUSION CULTURES

Bacteria are widely recognized for their rapid rate of reproduction. Great numbers may be secured by fission, which may occur every 15 to 30 minutes. A quantity of decaying grass should be placed in a beaker with water. The contents should be boiled for 15 minutes or longer. Cool the debris in an uncovered container until it settles to the bottom. Examine a drop of the liquid with the high power (4mm.) of the microscope. Very few organisms, if any, will be found at this examination. Study the solution again with a compound microscope after 24, 48, 72, 96, 120 and 144 hours. Look for bacillus, coccus, and spirillum types. Most of these will be extremely small and will require careful lighting and focusing. The numbers found from the third to sixth day are usually much greater than the number found the first day.

MAINTAINING STOCK CULTURES OF BACTERIA

Most cultures of organisms used in bacteriological experiments may be obtained from the American Type Culture Collection, Georgetown University School of Medicine, 3900 Reservoir Road, Washington, D.C.

Stock cultures of all aerobic bacteria may be maintained as slant or stab cultures (in ½-oz. screw-capped bottles or regular test tubes) in glucose (0.5 percent yeast infusion [or extract] agar or Difco Stock Culture Agar). These stocks should be transferred once a month. Anaerobic cultures may be grown in meat infusion with meat particles. Molds may be kept viable on potato glucose medium. They should be refrigerated only after sporulation is evident. After the incubation period, all stocks are maintained at refrigerator temperature.

BROTH CULTURES OF BACTERIA FOR CLASS USE

In many experiments, the materials list includes "broth cultures of (a certain type of bacteria)." These cultures are prepared commonly by inoculating a tube of glucose yeast infusion broth (or nutrient broth). After growth is evident (usually 16 to 24 hours) and a gram-stain check for purity is done, the assistant makes a transfer to one or more screw-capped bottles of the same medium. These bottles contain sufficient broth to permit the assistant to later on dispense approximately 5 ml. of culture to each pair (or four) students. After the bottle culture has grown, the broth for the required number of tubes for the class is pipetted to sterile, cotton-plugged tubes. This system of preparing bulk cultures ensures uniformity and represents a considerable saving of time compared with the inoculation of the individual tubes.

FERN PROTHALLIA, MOSS PROTONEMATA, AND MARCHANTIA

These may be cultivated on agar plates. The agar plates are prepared as follows: Mix 29 grams of agar with a small quantity of distilled water, shake well, and allow the mixture to stand for several hours until the agar has settled to the bottom of the container. Decant as much water as possible. Next, add more distilled water and repeat this process. This washes out much of the organic matter that can support the growth of bacteria. Filter through filter paper. Discard the filtrate. The agar retained on the filter paper is then placed in a flask and the following nutrient solution (Beyernick's, modified) is added:

Ammonium nitrate .... 0.5 gm.

Monobasic potassium phosphate .... 0.2 gm.

Magnesium sulfate .... 0.2 gm.

Calcium chloride .... 0.1 gm.

Ferric chloride .... few drops of 1% solution

Distilled water .... 100 cc.

Plug the flask with cotton and sterilize it, along with several dozen Petri dishes, in the autoclave (15 pounds for 15 minutes). Pour deep plates. After solidification of the medium, the plates may be seeded with fern spores to secure fern prothallia, moss spores for protonemata, or gemmules for Marchantia.

RULES FOR HANDLING PURCHASED CULTURES

1. When a shipment containing live cultures arrives in the department, the assistant should pour the contents of the shipping jar into a finger bowl, Petri dish, or similar container. Allow sufficient time for the contents to settle to the bottom. The bowl or dish should then be carefully placed on the stage of a binocular dissecting microscope for observation of the particular organism. With a pipette, a single specimen or even a group of organisms can be easily and quickly picked up and placed on a slide when the assistant is ready to supply specimens to each student for study.

2. After examination, the lid should be placed lightly over the container to prevent evaporation and to provide needed aeration until used.

3. If organisms appear dead or inactive upon first inspection, aerate the contents by forcing air back and forth through the medium with a pipette.

4. Always use new or chemically clean pipettes for removing samples of organisms from containers.

5. Do not place cultures in direct sunlight or in any situation of extreme heat or cold.

6. Students should be regularly warned against contaminating or accidentally killing a culture.

7. Agitation of the culture should be avoided since this scatters the organisms. *Amoeba* are usually found concentrated on the bottom. *Euglena* and *Volvox* are found toward the light. *Paramecium* will be concentrated on the surface of the liquid.

8. Use the binocular dissecting microscope in order to collect samples that contain numerous specimens.

9. Avoid all experimentation or subcultivation until the regular laboratory exercises have been completed.

GENERAL CARE OF PROTOZOAN CULTURES

Protozoan cultures differ in their reactions to stimuli and environmental changes. If there is a sudden drop in temperature, some forms will become sluggish in their movements; if they are undergoing a mitotic division or are actively feeding, they tend to "ball up." There is nothing wrong with such an organism that a short period of time will not clear up. Any protozoan that is dead will have disintegrated, and no discernible form will be visible upon examination. Some forms often congregate in masses around the perimeter at the bottom of their shipping bottles, and in such state they can be overlooked until the bottle contents are shaken lightly. A protozoan culture may be partially covered by metabolic debris which normally will develop in all cultures.

All protozoan culture jars should be left quiet without agitation for a period of 15 to 20 minutes before the laboratory period begins. When specimens are removed, the jar should be held steadily on the table top with one hand (lifting the jar up may scatter some specimens), and a small amount of the contents from the bottom of the jar should be drawn very carefully into a pipette. One drop will usually contain many more organisms than are needed for one good slide mount. This operation must be carried out by the assistant if his beginning students have not learned the techniques of mounting living cultures.

Upon receipt of protozoan cultures, the surface, bottom, and sides of the culture bottle should be examined with the dissecting microscope. The bottle should be shaken carefully and the contents poured into a finger bowl. After a few minutes, many specimens can be picked up with a pipette and placed on a slide for examination.

Some forms will require exposure to a source of light. In a short time, the organisms will collect on the lighted side of the container. They can then be easily removed with a pipette.

Protozoan cultures that are to be kept overnight for use at later laboratory periods should be aerated and stored in a cool location with the lids lightly placed over the containers.

SPECIFIC METHODS FOR CULTURING PROTOZOA

Protozoa are best cultured under conditions of moderate light, a temperature of 70° F., and a pH approximating neutrality or slightly on the alkaline side. Cultures are maintained in culture dishes (4½" x 2"). These dishes may be stacked on top of one another. The top dish on each stack is left empty and serves as a cover. The quantity of medium per bowl should be 200 cc.

Cloudy cultures may be cleaned for clear viewing by allowing the protozoans to settle to the bottom, decanting the top half of the water, and replacing it with spring water, boiled aerated tap water, or distilled water. Repeat this operation several times if necessary. Let the culture jars remain still and quiet for about five minutes for *Amoeba proteus*, *Chaos Chaos*, *Didinium*, and *Arcella*. For *Blepharisma*, *Spirostomum*, *Dileptus*, *Peranema*, and *Paramecium buraria*, allow one hour. *Eudorina*, *Pandorina*, *Gonium*, and *Volvox* should be exposed to light.

To concentrate many protozoans such as *Chaos chaos*, *Amoeba proteus*, *Didinium*, and *Stentor* into the center of the container, simply move the jar carefully in a circular fashion. Polyvinyl alcohol, completely hydrolyzed and in 14 percent solution, and methyl cellulose in 10 percent solution will usually prove satisfactory for quieting protozoa.

Sometimes *Amoeba proteus* and *Chaos chaos* arrive in an unexpanded and cloudy condition. Clean the cultures until food and detritus have been almost completely removed. In a few minutes the amoebae should expand and show active movement.

CULTURING INVERTEBRATES IN GENERAL

Laboratory conditions for the culture of various invertebrates are much the same as those for protozoa. Optimum conditions may vary somewhat from those found in the average laboratory, but such variation will not be serious enough in most instances to cause difficulty. High summer temperatures probably cause the most trouble. The optimum temperature for most invertebrates is 70° F.

HYDRA

Hydra shipments must be opened as soon as possible. The liquid should be aerated by forcing air back and forth. *Hydra* should be used immediately in the laboratory. If the laboratory exercise must be extended over a period of several days, the water in the bottle must be changed and arrangements made for feeding the *Hydra* with *Daphnia*, annelid worms, or copepods. *Hydra* must not be kept in city tap water. Tap water causes death, as indicated by a contraction of tentacles and body column. Only spring, pond, well, or aged water should be used.

They should be kept at a room temperature of about 60° to 75° F. Budding *Hydra* should be handled very carefully. The buds may be near maturity and about ready to drop off. As the hydra population increases, a large number of daphnids must be added daily. The daphnids should be free of organic debris in order to prevent fouling the water. Fresh spring water should be used to replace that in the cultures every day. Daphnids must be seined from stock cultures with an aquarium net and washed with spring water before being given to the *Hydra*. The cultures of *Hydra* should be kept in a dimly lighted environment. Too much light favors development of algae on the walls of culture containers.

BROWN AND BLACK PLANARIA

After the animals are received, they need not be fed for a week. If they are to be maintained for any length of time they should be taken out of their culture jars and put in 8-inch glass culture dishes or a 20- x 12- x 2-inch enamel-lined dissecting pan at normal room temperatures. Quart jars or bottles with small openings should not be used, since they reduce the oxygen content.

Water in the containers should be routinely changed every two or three days. The animals should be removed from the containers and the culture dishes should be washed free of slime and debris. Only spring water should be used in the cultures. Distilled water should be avoided.

Hard-boiled egg yolk is the best food for planaria. The amount depends on the number of animals: half a yolk for 500 animals or a pea-sized piece for 50. They should not be overfed. They should be allowed to feed for 30 minutes. The remaining food should be removed in order to prevent a rapid increase of bacteria. A feeding once each week is usually sufficient.

Planaria should not be fed or handled when they are undergoing a sexual cycle. When the cocoons are deposited they should be carefully removed and placed in culture dishes containing spring water. The water for the cocoons should be changed every two or three days.

The cocoon will break open in about two weeks. Each cocoon usually hatches about four or five planaria.

Maintenance is about the same as for the adult except that much less egg yolk is used. Fragments about the size of a pencil lead will generally be sufficient.

If the planaria are used for regeneration experiments, they should be cut with a sharp scalpel or scissors. Each segment should be put in a separate container, and only spring water should be used in the containers. The water should be changed every two or three days. About seven days are required for new heads and tails to appear on the segments. The segments should not be fed until the new part has completely formed on the animals. Only minute pieces of egg should be used. Maintenance and care are the same as described for the normal adult.

MEALWORMS

An open-top metal container such as a lard can or storage drum is used. The size of the container will depend on the number of mealworms cultured and the length of time the culture is to be maintained. Directions: Spread a layer of shredded paper over the bottom of the container. Next, sprinkle about a pound of a one-to-one mixture of "Red Dog" meal and bran into and on top of the shredded paper. Then use screen wire to cover the top of the can or drum. Maintain the container at room temperature. No provision for water is necessary. Feed the worms every four to five months by adding a new layer of shredded paper containing meal and bran.

BRINE SHRIMP

Any type of glass container with a 1-pint capacity may serve as the culture container. Fill to within 2 inches of the top with a 1 percent solution of noniodized NaCl.

The amount of brine shrimp eggs necessary depends upon the size of the container. For a pint jar, use up to ¼ teaspoon of eggs; for a quart jar up to ½ teaspoon; for one gallon up to 1 teaspoon; and for a 3-gallon jar up to 1 tablespoon.

Maintain the arrangement at normal room temperature. The percentage of hatching may be increased by aerating the jar to maintain the eggs in complete circulation at all times. The eggs will hatch in 24 to 36 hours.

DAPHNIA

These animals should not be kept in tap water, since it may be toxic. There is a direct relationship between the volume of water and the number of *Daphnia* that will survive.

A suspension of egg yolk for nourishment in the culture water is adequate for both battery-jar cultures and for those in aquarium tanks of various sizes.

Sediment that forms in the bottom of the culture tank should not be removed. This sediment probably contains many viable eggs that will hatch when additional food and fresh water are needed.

Daphnia will remain active and will reproduce within a range of 70° to 80° F.

DROSOPHILA

Drosophila melanogaster has achieved prominence in the field of genetics. This insect can be used readily to demonstrate the principles of heredity, such as the Mendelian ratio, sex linkage, dominance, and variation. Its cycle is completed in ten days; consequently many generations of flies are produced in a short period. This is a most helpful factor when breeding for pure strains or specific mutations.

Many advancements have been made with methods of culturing *Drosophila*. A culture of wild *Drosophila* can be started simply by allowing a dish containing some ripe banana to stand open. The flies are attracted to the food, upon which they lay their eggs. The culture thus begun can be continued by transferring the larvae and pupae to other banana preparations. The use of the banana medium dates back to the beginning of the study of Drosophila. However, superior culture methods have now replaced the banana method.

Various media are available for purchase by the department. Arrangements should be made for securing Drosophila from a biological supply house for use in laboratory studies. With each shipment, the assistant should receive detailed information leaflets regarding medium preparation, methods of mating the flies, and making crosses. Detailed directions for working with Drosophila will be found in Turtox Service Leaflet Number 15.

Chapter VI
Formulas and Solutions

PURPOSES

1. To provide for the assistant the specific compositions of various chemical preparations utilized in the department and laboratory.

2. To provide specific directions for production of these chemical preparations,

3. To stimulate in the assistant a broader appreciation for the applications of chemistry in biology.

CHEMICAL PREPARATIONS IN THE DEPARTMENT AND IN THE LABORATORY

At various times the assistant and staff have need for particular chemical preparations to be used for specific purposes in departmental and laboratory work. Such preparations may be used for demonstrating the finer structure of the nucleus or cytoplasm, for staining a given portion of the cell, for fixing an organism to a slide, or for comparing the detailed appearance of plant or animal structures.

Full information regarding the composition, purposes, methods of preparation and application of stains and various biological reagents would comprise a volume itself. The following selected chemical preparations are presented as representative compositions with which the assistant may become acquainted profitably as a part of his general proficiency. There will be times when the assistant may prepare these to be used by himself, by students, or by the teaching staff. There will be other times when such preparations may better be purchased from a biological supply house, using the company catalog for making selections, or from a pharmacist. The assistant will find Brauer's *Laboratory Direction for Histological Techniques* extremely helpful with such information as stain composition and histological procedures.

GENERAL PERCENTAGE RULE FOR PREPARATION OF SOLUTIONS

1. A ratio and proportion relationship is used.
2. Example: Prepare 4 liters of a 0.6 percent saline solution.
3. Drug or chemical: amount of total solution wanted = percent:100

$$x:4000 \text{ ml.} = 0.6:100$$
$$x = 24 \text{ gm. of sodium chloride}$$

4. In this case, the assistant would use 24 gm. of sodium chloride to make 4 liters of a .6 percent saline solution.

ACID CLEANSER

A good acid cleanser is made by mixing 400 cc. of commercial sulfuric acid with enough potassium or sodium bichromate to make a saturated solution. This reagent can be re-used several times to clean glassware. When a greenish color develops, it has lost its cleaning properties.

ABSOLUTE ALCOHOL FROM 95 PERCENT ALCOHOL

Directions: Heat some powdered copper sulfate in a crystallizing dish to evaporate the water of crystallization. There is a color change from blue powder to a whitish powder. The resulting powder should be poured into the 95 percent alcohol (approximately 10 parts alcohol to 1 part copper sulfate). Shake the mixture and place in a tightly covered container from 3 to 4 hours. After the copper has settled out, decant the clear liquid into a clean, dry bottle. This is absolute alcohol. Keep tightly stoppered during storage.

ACETOCARMINE STAIN (BELLING'S SOLUTION)

Directions: Heat to the boiling point a 45 percent solution of glacial acetic acid; add an excess of carmine; allow to cool and filter.

ALCOHOL-FORMALIN-ACETIC ACID (A.F.A.)

70 percent alcohol ....90 cc.
Commercial formalin ....10 cc.
Glacial acetic acid .... 2 cc.

This is an excellent fixative for intestinal worms that are to be mounted *in toto*. Requires no washing. If objects are to be stained *in toto*, go into water through 35 percent alcohol.

ALLEN'S SOLUTION B

The best reagent for the fixation and demonstration of mammalian and avian chromosomes. This fixation should be done at body temperature. It is also good for the chromosome fixation of invertebrates.

Freshly prepared Bouin's warmed to
  38° Centigrade ....100 cc.
Add and dissolve:
Chromic acid crystals ....1.5 gm.
Urea crystals ....2.0 gm.

AQUEOUS HEMATOXYLIN

Heat 100 cc. distilled water to the boiling point; remove from flame; add 0.2 gm. Hematoxylin crystals when boiling stops. The solution is ready for use as soon as it cools.

BENEDICT'S SOLUTION

Benedict's solution is made as follows: Add 173 gm. of sodium citrate and 100 gm. of anhydrous sodium carbonate to 600 cc. of distilled water and heat until the chemicals are dissolved. Filter this solution. Next, add 17.3 g. of copper sulfate to 150 cc. of distilled water. After the copper sulfate has dissolved, slowly add this solution to the sodium citrate and sodium carbonate solution, stirring constantly. Add enough distilled water to bring the whole solution up to 1 liter. When this solution is mixed with a sugar solution and heated, a brick-red color develops. When no sugar is present the solution remains blue upon heating.

BOUIN'S FLUID

Saturated aqueous solution picric acid . . . . .75 cc.
Commercial formalin . . . . .20 cc.
Glacial acetic acid . . . . 5 cc.
This is a standard fixing agent. There is no danger of overfixing. From Bouin's, transfer tissues directly to 50 or 70 percent alcohol, changing the alcohol several times before continuing dehydration.

BUFFER SOLUTIONS

Two solutions are used which are mixed at the time of use in the proper proportions to give the pH value desired. A pH of from 6.4 to 6.8 is desirable.

Solution A

Sodium phosphate (monobasic) Na_2PO_4 . . . . .4.539 gms.
Water, doubly distilled . . . . .500 ml.

Solution B

Potassium phosphate (monobasic) KH_2PO_4 . . . .4.539 gms.
Water, doubly distilled . . . . .500 ml.
After mixing solutions A and B for use, the mixture should be diluted with doubly distilled water in a 2:1 ratio.

DELAFIELD'S HEMATOXYLIN

Directions: Saturate 100 cc. of distilled water with ammonia alum (aluminum ammonium sulfate); filter. Dissolve 1 gm. hematoxylin crystals in 6 cc. absolute alcohol. Add the hematoxylin solution drop by drop to the ammonia alum solution. Place in a beaker, cover with cheesecloth, and leave in a well-lighted place for fifteen days. Then add 25 cc. methyl alcohol and the same amount of glycerin. The resulting solution should have a dark bluish-purple color. It is ready for use after filtering. If not contaminated, this dye will remain in good condition for a year or more.

DILUTE ALCOHOL FROM 95 PERCENT ALCOHOL

Various percentages of alcohol dilutions can better be made from 95 percent stock alcohol than from the more expensive 100 percent alcohol. In producing a desired percentage of alcohol, the assistant should remember that the needed amount of 95 percent alcohol in cubic centimenters is the same as the percentage dilution of alcohol desired. For example, if a 70 percent solution of alcohol were desired, the assistant would use 70 cc. of 95 percent alcohol.

The amount of distilled water necessary to add to the 95 percent alcohol to produce the proper dilution is determined by subtracting the desired percentage of alcohol (in this case 70 percent) from 95 percent. This subtraction gives 25 cc. of distilled water to be added to 70 cc. of 95 percent alcohol in order to produce 95 cc. of 70 percent alcohol. This same general dilution principle applies for any desired dilution of alcohol.

EHRLICK'S ACID HEMATOXYLIN (PROGRESSIVE STAIN)

Hematoxylin (certified) ....2 gms.
Glacial Acetic Acid ....10 cc.
Glycerine, C.P. ....100 cc.
Absolute alcohol ....100 cc.
Potassium alum (Aluminum potassium sulfate) ..10 gms.
Water, distilled ....100 ml.

Directions: Grind the potassium alum in a mortar and dissolve it in the water with the aid of heat. Dissolve the hematoxylin in the glacial acetic acid with about 25 cc. of the absolute alcohol and stir. After the hematoxylin is dissolved, pour into a flask, adding the glycerine while agitating the flask. Rinse the glycerine container with the remainder of the absolute alcohol and add to the stain solution, continuing to agitate the solution.

Add the warm or slightly hot alum solution to the stain a little at a time while continuing to stir.

Place the freshly prepared stain in a wide-mouthed jar stoppered loosely with a wad of cotton and cover with a single thickness of cheesecloth. Set the solution in a well-lighted place. To hasten the ripening, the solution should be agitated daily. This process usually requires from two weeks to a month or longer. When "ripe," stain will become dark. At this time the stopper should be removed and the jar sealed. The stain will be ready for use after several months.

EMBALMING FLUID

Carbolic Acid (melted crystals) .... 2.5 parts
Formalin (40 percent) .... 1.5 parts
Glycerine .... 10.0 parts
Water .... 86.0 parts

Mix and store until used.

EOSIN Y

For a supply of 5 percent aqueous solution of Eosin Y, use 10 cc.
Eosin diluted with 90 cc. 25 percent ethyl alcohol.

Used as a counterstain with alum hematoxylin.

FEHLING'S SOLUTION

Fehling's solution is made by mixing A and B each time just before the solution is used. The A and B solutions are made as follows:
Solution A: Copper sulfate, 17.3 gm. made up to 250 cc. with distilled water. Solution B: Sodium potassium tartrate (Rochelle salts),
86.5 gm. to 125 cc. distilled water; sodium hydroxide, 25 gm. to 125
cc. distilled water.

When parts A and B are mixed and added to a sugar solution
and the mixture heated, a reddish-brown (or yellow) precipitate of
cuprous oxide is produced. Any increase in quantity of precipitate
indicates an increase in the concentration of the sugar.

FORMALIN-ALCOHOL-ACETIC ACID (F.A.A.)

A simple fixative or preservative for simpler plant and animal preparations which is advantageous for the following reasons: materials
are easily procured; it penetrates rapidly; it fixes large volumes of
tissue compared to volume of liquid; it lasts indefinitely; tissue fixed
in it need not be washed in water before dehydration but may be
transferred directly to 70 percent alcohol (ethyl or grain); tissues
may be kept in this agent indefinitely without injury. F.A.A. is a
particularly satisfactory preservative for museum specimens.

The following two formulas are in common use:

(1) Alcohol (ethyl or grain) 50 percent .... 90 cc.
    Formalin (commercial) .... 5 cc.
    Glacial acetic acid .... 5 cc.
(2) Alcohol (ethyl or grain) 70 percent .... 85 cc.
    Formalin (commercial) .... 10 cc.
    Glacial acetic acid .... 5 cc.

FORMALDEHYDE DILUTIONS

The appropriate dilution of formaldehyde to be used as a general fixative and preservative in the department is made from the 40 percent full-strength formaldehyde stock solution known as Formalin. This may be purchased in the gallon, carboy, or drum quantity. Instant Formalin Powder and Buffer may also be purchased, with specific directions for its use.

A 5 percent formalin solution is produced with 5 cc. stock formaldehyde and 95 cc. distilled water. A 10 percent formalin solution is produced by mixing 10 cc. stock formaldehyde with 90 cc. distilled water.

IODINE SOLUTION

A few crystals of potassium iodide are placed in 100 ml. of distilled water. Stir. Add iodine crystals until the water is colored yellow.

IODOEOSIN SOLUTION

Eosin .... 0.5 gm.
Potassium Iodide .... 1.0 gm.
Distilled water .... 100 ml.
Filter and store for use.

JEFFREY'S MACERATION SOLUTION

(A) Nitric Acid (10 percent in water) .... 100 cc.
(B) Chromic Acid (10 percent in water) .... 100 cc.
Solutions A and B should be mixed just before using for macerating stems, roots, and leaves.

KYMOGRAPH SHELLAC

Alcohol 95 percent .... 85 parts
Methyl Alcohol .... 15 parts

Put white shellac into a large bottle; add above solution ("methylated spirits") to fill. Shake well. Let stand for 24 hours to settle; decent. The residue of shellac may be re-used many times.

LOCKE'S SOLUTION

Sodium chloride .... 9.0 gm.
Potassium chloride .... 0.42 gm.
Calcium chloride .... 0.24 gm.
Glucose .... 0.20 gm.
Distilled water .... enough to make 1,000 ml.

Store and use.

All solutions containing glucose should be made in small quantities, kept in a cool place, and made frequently. Glucose deteriorates quickly.

MACERATION SOLUTIONS

(A) Chromic Acid 0.1 percent
(B) Alcohol 30 percent
(C) Nitric Acid 30 percent

(A) Chromic acid 0.1 percent

This solution is good for skeletal muscle. The material should be cut into small pieces, which are then covered with the solution for 18 to 24 hours.

(B) Alcohol 30 percent

Good for smooth muscle tissue. Cut muscle tissue into small pieces and let them stand in the alcohol for 12 to 18 hours.

(C) Nitric acid 30 percent

Used for bone, muscle, and connective tissues. It leaves the central nervous system intact. The animal is killed, skinned, and eviscerated, then placed flat in a glass container and covered with acid for 36 hours. The macerated tissue may be removed by holding tissues carefully under cold running water. Structures should then be mounted in suitable containers in 5 percent formalin solution.

MANN'S HEMATEIN

This stain is made up like Ehrlich's hematoxylin except that hematein is used instead of hematoxylin. Hematein is the oxidation product of hemotoxylin and should not require ripening; however, some ripening renders better results.

METHYLENE BLUE SOLUTION

Methylene blue .... 0.5 gm.
Distilled water .... 100 cc.
Filter and store for use.

NEUTRAL RED

A solution of approximately 5 percent neutral red in distilled water is a saturated solution. However, a much more dilute solution is commonly used, especially in vital staining. Neutral red is not toxic to living cells.

NUTRIENT AGAR MEDIUM

One liter of distilled water is heated to the boiling point Five gm. of peptone and 3 gm. of powdered yeast extract (or 3 gm. of meat extract) are then added to the water. This is stirred until peptones and yeast have dissolved. Add 1 ml. of brom-thymol-blue indicator solution (concentrated stock solution). While continuously stirring, add slowly just enough 4 percent sodium hydroxide solution (or if medium is blue, 4 percent hydrochloric acid solution) to turn the color of the medium to a bluish-green. Then add 20 gm. of sugar. Boil until the agar is dissolved. While it is still hot, filter through moist filter paper or nonabsorbent cotton into small flasks. Insert cotton plugs and sterilize the flasks in the autoclave (a pressure cooker may be used) for 20 minutes at 120° C.

After the agar medium has been sterilized, but before it has cooled to below 40° C., it may be poured into sterile Petri dishes. The mouth of each flask should be flamed just before the medium is poured from it. The cover of the Petri dish should be tilted up only momentarily for pouring. About 10 ml. should be poured into each dish.

RINGER'S SOLUTION (COLD-BLOODED)

Sodlum chloride .... 6.0 gm.
Potassium chloride .... 0.14 gm.
Calcium chloride .... 0.12 gm.
Sodium bicarbonate .... 0.20 gm.
Distilled water .... enough to make 1,000 ml.
Store and use.

RINGER'S SOLUTION (WARM-BLOODED)

Sodium chloride .... 8.5 gm.
Potassium chloride .... 0.42 gm.
Calcium chloride .... 0.24 gm.
Glucose .... enough to make 1,000 ml.
Store and use.

SAFRANIN Y

Safranin Y crystals .... 1 gm.
Alcohol (50 percent) .... 100 cc.
Store and use.

SKIN-PRESERVING FORMULA

White arsenic (1 lb. dissolved in 1 pint of water) painted on the inside of the skin will preserve the skin. White arsenic may be mixed with powdered alum in equal proportions and dusted heavily over the inner surface of the skin while skin is still moist. It may be rubbed into the skin and the excess dusted off after the skin dries. This may also be made into a solution and painted on the skin. The solution is best if the skin has become too dry to hold the powder.

SUDAN III

Acetone .... 50 parts
Alcohol .... 50 parts

Saturate with Sudan III
Store and use.

WRIGHT'S STAIN

Use Coleman's and Bell's or National Aniline Company's Certified Dye.

Directions: Dissolve 20 mg. of the dye in 100 ml. of acetone-free methyl alcohol (specific for blood work). Weigh out the dye and place into an absolutely clean, dry beaker previously rinsed in acetone-free methyl alcohol. Add the alcohol and stir or grind the dye into the solution. Put the solution into a dry, clean amber bottle previously cleaned with alcohol. Stopper the bottle and let it stand 24 hours. Shake it well at intervals. The next day filter the solution into a clean, dry beaker previously cleaned with methyl alcohol and return the dye solution to the bottle, which should also have been rinsed with the alcohol. Keep it well stoppered or capped with a patent cap.

Chapter VII
Practical Summaries and Tables

PURPOSES

1. To provide in summary form a comprehensive selection of practical information,

2. To encourage the assistant to secure additional summaries for supplementing the initial selection,

3. To provide the assistant a source of answers to questions often presented by students in the department and in the laboratory.

I Summary of the Number of Animal Species.
Over 1,000,000 Animals Species

a. Arthropods 900,000
b. Mollusks 45,000
c. Chordates 45,000
d. Protozoans 30,000
e. Worm-like phyla 38,000
f. Other invertebrates 21,000

II Summary of the Number of Plant Species.
About 350,000 Plant Species

a. Flowering Plants 250,000
b. Ferns, Conifers, etc. 10,000
c. Mosses and Liverworts 23,000
d. Algae, Fungi, etc. 60,000

III Common and Scientific Names of Selected Plants and Animals of Field and Laboratory.

Edible mushroom—*Agaricus campestris*
Kidney bean—*Phaseolus vulgaris*
Sunflower—*Helianthus annuus*
Indian corn—*Zea mays*
Bread mold—*Rhizopus nigricans*
Corn smut—*Ustilago zeae*
Wheat rust—*Puccinia graminis*
Jellyfish—*Aurelia aurita*
Star coral—*Siderastraea galaxea*
Hydroid coral—*Stylaster sanguinea*
Vinegar eel—*Turbatrix aceti*
American hookworm—*Necator americanus*
Trichina worm—*Trichinella spiralis*
Garden nematode—*Heterodera radicicola*
Common starfish—*Asterias forbesi*
Purple sea urchin—*Arbacia punctulata*
Sand dollar—*Echinarachnius parma*
Sea cucumber—*Thyone briareus*
Sandworm—*Nereis virens*
Snail—*Helix pomatia*
Fresh water clam—*Lampsilis anodontoides*
Shipworm—*Toredo navalis*
Sowbug—*Porcellio laevis*
Water flea—*Daphnia pulex*
Fairy shrimp—*Branchinecta packardii*
King crab—*Limulus polyphemus*
Human itch mite—*Sarcoptes scabiei*
Hair follicle mite—*Demodex folliculorum*
Sea squirt—*Molgula manhattensis*
Spiny dogfish shark—*Squalus acanthias*
Sawfish—*Pristis antiquorum*
Small-mouth bass—*Micropterus dolomieu*
Yellow perch—*Perca flavescens*
Bullfrog—*Rana catesbiana*
Red-spotted newt—*Triturus viridescens*
Tiger salamander — *Ambystoma tigrinum*

Hellbender salamander—*Cryptobranchus allegheniensis*
Mudpuppy—*Necturus maculosus*
Horned toad—*Phrynosoma cornutum*
Giant collared lizard—*Crotaphytus collaris*
Black snake—*Zamenis constrictor*
Box turtle—*Cistudo carolina*
True chameleon—*Chameleon vulgaris*
American alligator—*Alligator mississippiensis*
Mourning dove—*Zenaidura macroura carolinensis*
Common tern—*Sterno hirundo*
Green heron—*Butorides virescens*
Ring-neck duck—*Marila collaris*
Brown pelican—*Pelicanus occidentalis*
Great horned owl—*Bubo virginianus virginianus*
Cardinal—*Cardinalis cardinalis*
Cedar waxwing—*Bombycilla cedrorum*
Orangutan—*Simia satyrus*
Llama—*Lama huanacos*
American bison—*Bison bison*
Bactrian camel—*Camelus bactrianus*
Beaver—*Castor canadensis*
Silverfish—*Lepisma saccharina*
Biting bird louse—*Menopon pallidum*
Body louse—*Pediculus corporis*
Head louse—*Pediculus capitis*
Termite—*Reticulitermes flavipes*
Bedbug—*Cimex lectularius*
Periodical cicada—*Tibicina septendecim*
Ladybird beetle—*Adalia bipunctata*
Clothes moth—*Tinea pellionella*
Silkworm—*Bombyx mori*
European corn borer—*Pyrausta nibilalis*
Dog and cat flea—*Ctenocephalus canis*
Horse roundworm—*Ascaris megalocephala*

Human roundworm—*Ascaris lumbricoides*
Crayfish—*Cambarus virilus*
Opossum—*Didelphys virginiana*
Cat—*Felis domesticas*
Monkey—*Rhesus macacus*
Man—*Homo sapiens*
Chinese primrose—*Primula sinensis*
Tomato—*Lycopersicum esculentum*
Onion—*Allium cepa*
American elm—*Ulmus americana*
White oak—*Quercus alba*
Fruit fly—*Drosophila melanogaster*
Earthworm—*Lumbricus terrestris*
Ostrich—*Struthio camelus*
Rattlesnake—*Crotalus horridus*
Lion—*Felis leo*
Lynx—*Lynx canadensis*
American bittern—*Botaurus lentiginosus*
Turkey buzzard—*Cathartes aura septentrionales*
Bald eagle—*Haliaeetus leucocephalus*
Kingfisher—*Ceryle alcyon*
Starling—*Sturnus vulgaris*
Mockingbird—*Mimus polyglottos leucopterus*
Tree frog—*Hyla cynerea*
Spanish mackerel—*Scomberomorus maculatus*
White mullet—*Mugil curema*
Muskrat—*Fiber zibethicus*
Common mouse—*Mus musculus*

Jack rabbit—*Lepus californicus*
Badger—*Taxidea taxus*
Atlantic walrus—*Odobenus rosmarus*
White polar bear—*Thalarctos maritimus*
Coyote—*Canis latrans*
Sperm whale—*Physeter catodon*
Brown bat—*Eptesicus fuscus*
Tomato fruitworm moth—*Heliothis obsoleta*
Alfalfa weevil—*Phytonomus porticus*
Black widow spider—*Latrodectus mactans*
Fresh-water rotifer—*Philodina roseola*
Shelf fungus—*Fomes applanatus*
Shaggy-mane mushroom—*Coprinus comatus*
Slime mold—*Physarum polycephalum*
Ash tree—*Fraxinus americana*
Ragweed—*Ambrosia artimisiifolia*
Cinnamon fern—*Osmunda cinnamomea*
Wood horsetail—*Equisetum sylvaticum*
Hemlock—*Tsuga canadensis*
Western yellow pine—*Pinus ponderosa*
Redwood—*Sequoia sempervirens*
Douglas fir—*Pseudotsuga taxifolia*
Red cedar—*Juniperus virginiana*
Apple tree—*Pyrus malus*
Pumpkin—*Cucurbita pepo*
Crimson clover—*Trifolium incarnatum*
Box elder—*Acer negundo*

IV Scientific Names of Economically Important Plants or Plant Products.

Penicillium notatum—Penicillin mold
Merulius lacrymans — Wood-rotting fungus
Penicillium roqueforti — Roquefort cheese mold
Lycopodium clavatum—Club moss
Coffea arabica—Coffee
Thea sinensis—Tea

Theobromo cacao—Cocoa
Vanilla planifolia—Vanilla bean
Citrus medica—Lemon tree
Gaultheria procumbens—Wintergreen plant
Mentha spicata—Spearmint herb
Mentha peperita—Peppermint herb
Citrus aurantium—Orange tree

Brassica nigra—Black mustard
Myristica fragrans—Nutmeg tree
Zingiber officinale—Ginger
Cinnamomum zeylanicum—Cinnamon
Caryophyllus aromaticus—Cloves
Capsicum annum—Red pepper
Piper nigrum—Black pepper
Salvia officinalis—Garden sage
Petroselinum sativum—Parsley
Thymus vulgaris—Thyme
Carum carvi—Caraway
Pimpinella anisum—Anise
Ricinus communis—Castor oil
Ferula assafoetida—Asafetida
Astragalus gummifer—Gum tragacanth

Glycyrrhiza glabra—Licorice
Datura stromonium—Jimson weed
Phytolacca decandra—Common poke-
weed
Conium maculatum—Water hemlock
Lobelia inflata—Indian tobacco plant
Kalmia latifolia—Mountain laurel
Amanita phalloides—Death cap
Papaver somniferum—Opium poppy
Nicotiana tabacum—Tobacco
Cinchona calisaya—Quinine
Rhus vernix—Poison sumac
Rhus toxicodendron—Poison ivy
Cypripedium parviflorum—Orchid

V Selected Pathological Conditions with Scientific Names of Causative Organisms.

Plant blight—Endothia parasitica
Bread mold—Rhizopus nigricans
Wheat rust—Puccinia graminis
Botulism—Clostridium botulinum
Boils, carbuncles, abscesses—Staphylo-
coccus aureus
Gaseous gangrene—Clostridium welchii
General infections—Streptococcus pyo-
genes
Tetanus ("lockjaw")—Clostridium tet-
ani
"Sore throat"—Streptococcus hemoly-
ticus
Whooping cough—Hemophilus pertus-
sis
Erysipelas—Streptococcus erysipelatis
Tularemia—Pasteurella tularense
Scarlet fever—Streptococcus scarla-
tinae
Plague ("Black death")—Pasteurella
pestis
Meningitis—Diplococcus intracellularis
Undulant fever—Brucella melitensis
Pneumonia—Diplococcus pneumoniae
Leprosy—Mycobacterium leprae
Anthrax—Bacillus anthracis
Tuberculosis—Mycobacterium tubercu-
losis

Diphtheria—Corynebacterium diphthe-
riae
Paratyphoid fever—Salmonella para-
typhi
North American blastomycosis—Blas-
tomyces dermatitidis
Moniliasis — Candida (monilia) albi-
cans
Coccidiomycosis — Coccidioides im-
mitis
Sporotrichosis—Sporotrichum schenkii
Foot ringworm—Tinea pedis
Scalp ringworm—Tinea capitis
Lumpy jaw—Actinomyces bovis
African sleeping sickness—Trypano-
soma gambiense
Human malaria—Plasmodium malaria
Schistosomiasis — Schistosoma japoni-
cum and others
Hookworm—Necator americanus
Pinworm—Entorobius vermicularis
Filariasis—Wuchereria bancrofti
Trichinosis—Trichinella spiralis
Human roundworm—Ascaris lumbri-
coides
Amebiasis—Endameba histolytica
Typhoid fever—Eberthella typhosa

VI Generic Names of Common Plant Forms in Field and Laboratory Studies.

Thallophyta: Group I
    Gleocapsa, Nostoc, Oscillatoria, Anabena
Group II
    Protococcus, Spirogyra, Ulothrix
Group III
    Laminaria, Fucus
Group IV
    Chondrus, Polysiphonia, Nemalion
Group V
    Stemonitis, Lycogala
Group VI
    Rhizopus, Saprolegnia, Peziza, Penicillium,
    Aspergillus

Bryophyta: Group I
    Marchantia, Porella
Group II
    Polytrichum, Sphagnum
Group III
    Lycopodium, Selaginella
Group IV
    Equisetum

Pteridophyta: *Pteridium, Polypodium*

Spermatophyta: Group I
    Pinus, Zamia
Group II
    Phaseolus, Helianthus, Zea

VII Generic Names of Common Animal Forms in Field and Laboratory Studies.

Protozoa: Group I
    Amoeba, Endamoeba, Actinophrys, Thallasicola
Group II
    Euglena, Peranema, Chilomonas, Synura
Group III
    Monocystis, Plasmodium
Group IV
    Paramecium, Vorticella, Stentor, Lacrymaria

	Group V
	Podophyrs
Porifera:	Group I
	Scypha, Leucosolenia
	Group II
	Euplectella
	Group III
	Euspongia
Coelenterata:	Group I
	Hydra, Obelia, Gonionemus
	Group II
	Aurelia
	Group III
	Metridium
Platyhelminthes:	Group I
	Planaria
	Group II
	Fasciola
	Group III
	Taenia
Nemathelminthes:	Group I
	Ascaris, Enterobius, Oxyuris
	Group II
	Necator, Ancylostoma, Syngamus
	Group III
	Wuchereria, Dracunculus
	Group IV
	Trichinella
Echinodermata:	Group I
	Asterias
	Group II
	Arbacia, Echinarachnius
	Group III
	Thyone
	Group IV
	Antedon
Annelida:	Group I
	Polygordius

	Group II
	Nereis
	Group III
	Hirudo
Mollusca:	Group I
	Chiton
	Group II
	Lymnea, Helix
	Group III
	Lampsilis, Toredo
	Group IV
	Loligo
	Group V
	Dentalium
Anthropoda:	Group I
	Palaemonetes, Daphnia, Cyclops
	Group II
	Peripatus
	Group III
	Apis, Achoreutes, Culex
	Group IV
	Attus, Sarcoptes, Phalangium
Chordata:	Group I
	Balanoglossus, Rhabdopleura
	Group II
	Molgula
	Group III
	Branchiostoma
	Group IV
	Squalus, Perca, Micropterus
	Group V
	Rana, Cryptobranchus, Necturus
	Group VI
	Crotaphytus, Zamenis, Cistudo, Chameleon, Alligator
	Group VII
	Sterno, Cardinalis, Bombycilla, Marila
	Group VIII
	Simia, Lama, Bison, Vulpes, Camelus, Ursus, Castor, Homo

VIII. Numbers of Chromosomes in Various Animals and Plants.

Animal	Number of Chromosomes per Body or Somatic Cell
Hydra (phylum, Coelenterata)	12
Horse roundworm (*Ascaris megalocephala*) (Nemathelminthes)	4
Human roundworm (*Ascaris Lumbricoides*) (Nemathelminthes)	48
Earthworm (*Lumbricus sp.*) (phylum, Annelida)	32
Leech (*Nephelis sp.*) (phylum, Annelida)	16
Crayfish (*Cambarus immunis*) (phylum, Arthropoda)	208
Fruit fly (*Drosophila sp.*) (phylum, Arthropoda)	8
House fly (*Musca sp.*) (phylum, Arthropda)	12
Mosquito (*Anopheles sp.*) (phylum, Arthropoda)	6
Cockroach (*Periplaneta sp.*) (phylum, Arthropoda)	34
Rabbit (*Lepus sp.*) (subphylum, Vertebrata)	44
Dog (*Canis sp.*) (subphylum, Vertebrata)	78
Horse (*Equus sp.*) (subphylum, Vertebrata)	60
Cat (*Felis domesticus*) (subphylum, Vertebrata)	38

Plants

Green Alga (*Spirogyra sp.*) (phylum, Thallophyta)	24
Peat moss (*Sphagnum sp.*) (phylum, Bryophyta)	40
Pine tree (*Pinus sp.*) (Gymnosperm)	24
Pea (*Pisum, sp.*) (Angiosperm)	14
Tomato (*Lycopersicum esculentum*) (Angiosperm)	24
Corn (*Zea mays*) (Angiosperm)	20
Onion (*Allium cepa*) (Angiosperm)	16
Lily (*Lilium sp.*) (Angiosperm)	24

IX Early Development Compared in Different Vertebrate Types.

Animal Type	Type of Egg	Cleavage	Blastula	Blastula Cavity	Method of Gastrulation	Comment on Gastrulation
Amphioxus	(little yolk) Isolecithal	Total; nearly equal	Sphere; wall a single layer	Spherical and large	Invagination; involution via blastopore	Early inner layer, a composite
Amphibians	Telolecithal (moderate yolk)	Total; unequal	Sphere; wall layered and unequal	Spherical and small; eccentric	Involution via blastopore	Germ layers separate from start
Birds	Telolecithal (massive yolk)	Partial; discoidal	Cell-disc, on massive yolk	Shallow; overlies yolk	Delamination; involution via primitive streak	Occurs in two stages
Mammals (except lowest)	Isolecithal (little yolk)	Total; nearly equal	Blastocyst, with inner cell mass	Merged with blastocyst cavity	Delamination; involution via primitive streak	Occurs in two stages

X The Germ-Layer Origin Of Human Tissues.

Ectoderm	Mesoderm	Entoderm
1. Epidermis, including: cutaneous glands; hair; nails; lens	1. Muscle (all types)	1. Pharynx, including: auditory tube; tonsils; thyroid; parathyroids; thymus
2. Epithelium of: sense organs; nasal cavity; sinuses; mouth, including: oral glands; enamel; anal canal	2. Connective tissue; cartilage; bone; notochord	2. Larynx; trachea; lungs
	3. Blood; bone marrow	
	4. Lymphoid tissue	3. Digestive tube, including associated glands
	5. Epithelium of: blood vessels; lymphatics	
	6. Body cavities	4. Bladder
	7. Kidney; ureter	
3. Nervous tissue, including: hypophysis; chromaffin tissue	8. Gonads; genital ducts	5. Vagina; vestibule
	9. Suprarenal cortex	
	10. Joint cavities	6. Urethra, including associated glands

XI Comparative Data Concerning Gestation In Mammals.

Animal	Gestation Period	No. in Litter
Opossum	13 days	8
Mouse, rat	20-22 days	6-8
Rabbit	32 days	6
Cat; dog; guinea pig	9 weeks	4-6
Sow	17 weeks	6-12
Sheep; goat	21 weeks	1-2
Macacus monkey	24 weeks	1
Man; manlike apes	38 weeks	1
Cow	40 weeks	1
Mare	48 weeks	1
Rhinoceros	18 months	1
Elephant	20 months	1

XII Anatomical Terms Applied to the Total or
Sectioned Organism.

a. Regions and Directions

1. *Aboral.* Pertaining to the region not associated with the mouth. The opposite of oral.

2. *Anterior.* The forward-moving or head end of a bilaterally symmetrical animal. Toward the head end; in front of. Foremost in locomotion. Opposite of posterior.

3. *Caudal.* Pertaining to the tail or posterior part of the body. Opposite of cephalic.

4. *Cephalic.* Pertaining to the head end. Opposite of caudal.

5. *Distal.* Away from the place or point of attachment; toward the periphery or the extremities of the body. Opposite of proximal.

6. *Dorsal.* Toward or pertaining to the back or the upper surface.

7. *Lateral.* On either side of the middle part of the body. Contrasted with medial.

8. *Medial* (median). On, near, toward, or pertaining to the middle the body. Contrasted with lateral.

9. *Oral.* Pertaining to the mouth (the oral surface is the surface containing the mouth).

10. *Peripheral.* Pertaining to the outer region or the edge of the body or part.

11. *Posterior.* The hinder part. Toward the hinder (tail) end; away from the head. Opposite of anterior.

12. *Proximal.* Nearer or toward the central part of the body. Opposite of distal.

13. *Ventral.* Toward or pertaining to the lower side or the belly; away from the back. Opposite of dorsal.

b. Axes

1. *Dorso-ventral axis.* From back or dorsal surface to under or ventral surface, and at right angles to longitudinal axis.

2. *Main or longitudinal axis.* A hypothetical line extending the length of the body from anterior to posterior end; or from oral (mouth) surface to aboral (opposite) surface in radial animals.

3. *Transverse axis.* From side to side at right angles to longitudinal and dorso-ventral axis.

c. Planes

1. *Frontal plane.* Any plane which includes a longitudinal and a transverse axis; hence, parallel to the front of the body in man or parallel to the ventral surface in any bilateral animal; at right angles to sagittal plane.

2. *Median or sagittal plane.* Divides the body into symmetrical right and left halves; pertains to the median vertical plane of the body; includes the longitudinal axis and any dorso-ventral axis. Any plane parallel to the sagittal is a para-sagittal plane.

3. *Para-sagittal plane.* Any plane parallel to the sagittal plane.

4. *Transverse plane.* Any plane which is at a right angle to a longitudinal axis; hence, at right angles to sagittal and frontal planes.

5. *Vertical plane.* A plane directed perpendicularly to the surface of a structure.

d. Symmetry

1. *Asymmetrical.* Any body or part that cannot be divided into two or more equivalent parts.

2. *Bilateral symmetry.* Having the body or a part that can be divided by one median (sagittal) plane into equivalent right and left halves, each a mirror image of the other.

3. *Radial symmetry.* Having similar equivalent parts (antimeres) arranged around a common central axis, as in a sea anemone or starfish.

4. *Symmetrical.* A body or part which can be divided into two or more equivalent parts.

e. Sections

1. *Coronal or Frontal Section.* Any section made by slicing parallel to the long axis and dividing the body or part into dorsal and ventral portions.

2. *Cross-section.* A section made by slicing the body or part from dorsal to ventral and side to side.

3. *Metamerism.* Having the body composed (externally, internally, or both) of a number of similar and homologous parts (somites, metameres). This condition is seen in annelids, arthropods, and chordates.

4. *Sagittal Section.* Any section produced by slicing the body or part into right and left halves.

XIII Dental Development.

Deciduous* Teeth (20 in number)	No.	Time** of Eruption in Months	Permanent Teeth (32 in number)	No.	Time** of Eruption in Years
Lower central incisors	2	5-9	First molars	4	6-7
Upper central incisors	2	8-12	Incisors	8	7-8
Upper lateral incisors	2	10-12	Biscuspids	8	9-10
Lower lateral incisors	2	12-15	Canines	4	12-14
Anterior molars	4	12-15	Second molors	4	12-15
Canines	4	18-24	Third molars	4	17-25
Posterior molars	4	24-30			

* An average child should have: 6 teeth at 1 year; 12 teeth at 1½ years; 16 teeth at 2 years; 20 teeth at 2½ years. ** Varies greatly.

XIV Basic Daily Diet Plan For Adults.
(Provides approximately 1,500 calories)

Milk	1 pt.
Meat, fish, or poultry	1 serving (3½ oz.)
Egg	1
Protein foods (additional)	1 egg ½ pt. milk or 1 oz. meat, fish or cheese
Vegetables	1 potato, med. size 2 servings (100 gm.) leafy, green, or yellow vegetables 1 serving (100 gm.) other vegetables
Fruits	1 serving (100 gm.) citrus fruit or juice, tomato or other rich sources of vitamin C 1 serving (100 gm.) noncitrus fruit
Butter or enriched margarine	½ oz.
Bread and cereal	4 slices whole grain or enriched bread, or 3 slices bread and 1 serving (½ cup) whole grain or enriched cereal

XV Gastric Contents.

Physiologic Normals:

Total acidity .... 50-100 degrees*
Free HCl .... 25-50 degrees
Combined HCl .... 10-15 degrees
Organic acids and acid salts .... 3-5 degrees

---

* Degrees are equivalent to the cc. of 0.1N sodium hydroxide required to neutralize 100 cc. of gastric contents.

XVI Cerebrospinal Fluid.

Physiologic Normals:

Volume .... approx. 130 cc.
Color .... colorless and clear
Specific gravity 1.003-1.008
Reaction .... alkaline
Protein 15-45   mg./100 cc.
Glucose 40-60   mg./100 cc.
Chloride (NaCl) .... 720-750 mg./100 cc.
Phosphate (inorganic) 1-2   mg./100 cc.
Calcium .... 4.5-5.5 mg./100 cc.
Cells 0-10   cu.mm.
Pressure .... 5-7.5   mm. of mercury
                                        100-200 mm. of water

XVII Blood.

Physiologic Normals:

Volume .... 7-9% body wt.
                                     (4,000-6,000 cc.)
pH 7.35-7.45
Erythrocytes .... 4,500,000-5,000,000/cu.mm.
Reticulocytes 0.8-1.0%
Leucocytes .... 5,000-10,000 cu.mm.
    Polymorphonuclear neutrophils 60-70%
    Lymphocytes 25-33%

Monocytes 2-6%
Eosinophils 1-3%
Basophils 0.25-0.5%
Platelets .... 200,000-400,000/cu.mm.
Hemoglobin (average for both sexes) .... 14-16 gm./100 cc.
Hematocrit average (men) .... 47% ±7%
Hematocrit average (women) .... 42% ±5%
Color Index 0.9-1.1
Volume Index 0.9-1.1
Mean corpuscular hemoglobin .... 80-94 cu. microns
                                                     27-32 micromicrograms
Mean. corp. hemo. concentration 32-38%
Bleeding time .... 1-3 min.
Coagulation time .... 6-12 min.
Clot retraction time .... begins in 1 hr.; complete in 24 hrs.
Sedimentation rate (Westergren,
  in 1st hr., men) .... 0.12 mm.
  (women) .... 0.20 mm.
C-Reactive Protein (CRP) .... less than 1 mm. precipitation
Prothrombin time (Quick) .... 10-15 sec.

XVIII The Circulation: In Health And In Various Forms Of Shock.

(Figures in parentheses represent typical values)

	Cardiac Output	Blood Volume	Hema- trocit	Blood Pressure
In Health	Normal (5.4 L./min.)	Normal (6.0 L.)	Normal (45%)	Normal (120/80)
Syncope	Normal	Normal	Normal	Low (70/50)
Wound Shock, Hemorrhage	Low (3.5 L./min.)	Low (3.1 L.)	Low (32%)	Low (70/40)
Burns	Low (3.0 L./min.)	Low (3.2 L.)	High (55%)	Variable; often no change (114/70)

Abdominal Injury, Dehydration	Low (3.2 L./min.)	Low (4.0 L.)	High (52%)	Moderately Low (80/50)
Medical (toxic) shock	Low (3.5 L./min.)	Normal	Normal	Low (70/50)

XIX Urine.

Physiologic Normals:

Average amount in 24 hr. ....1,200-1,500 cc.
Reaction to litmus .... faintly acid
Specific gravity 1.005-1.022
Color ....pale straw to amber

Constituents (in 24-hr. specimen)

Urea .... 20.0-30.0 gm.
Uric Acid .... 0.6- 0.75 gm.
Total nitrogen .... 10.0-16.0 gm.
Ammonia .... 0.5-15.0 gm.
Chlorides ....10.0-15.0 gm.
Phosphate .... 2.0- 4.0 gm.
Total sulfur .... 1.0- 3.5 gm.
Creatinine .... 0.3- 0.45 gm.
17-Ketosteroids, average (adult women) ... 5.0-15.0 mg./24 hr.
17-Ketosteroids, average (adult men) ...... 5.0-27.0 mg./24 hr.
Total solids ....50.0-70.0 gm.
Total acidity ....equiv. to 400-600 cc. of 0.1N sodium hydroxide

XX Transformation Tables.

a. Length

English	Metric
1 foot	= 30.48 centimeters
1 inch	= 2.54 centimeters
39.37 inches	= 1 meter
0.39 inch	= 1 centimeter
0.039 inch	= 1 millimeter

b. Capacity

1 qt. (dry)   = 1.1 liters
1 qt. (liquid) = 0.94 liter
1 ounce (fluid) = 28.3 cc. milliliters

c. Weight

1 gram = 0.06 gram
1 dram (avdp.) = 1.77 grams
1 ounce (avdp.) = 28.3 grams
1 pound (avdp.) = 453.5 grams
2.2 pounds (avdp.) = 1 kilogram

d. Temperature

60 degrees C. = 140.0 degrees F.
50 degrees C. = 122.0 degrees F.
40 degrees C. = 104.0 degrees F.
30 degrees C. = 86.0 degrees F.
20 degrees C. = 68.0 degrees F.
10 degrees C. = 50.0 degrees F.
 0 degrees C. = 32.0 degrees F.
−5 degrees C. = 23.0 degrees F.

e. Temperature Conversion Formulas

To convert centigrade (°C.) to Fahrenheit (°F.), multiply °C. by 1.8 and add 32; thus, for 20°C., 20 × 1.8 + 32 equals 68°F. To convert °F. to °C. subtract 3 and multiply by 0.55.

XXI Prefixes of The Metric System.

Mega-	.....	one million	.... 10^6	 1,000,000
Myria-	.....	ten thousand	... 10^4	 10,000
Kilo-	....	one thousand	... 10^3	 1,000
Hecta-	.....	one hundred	... 10^2	100
Deka-	.....	ten	.... 10^1	10
(none)	....	one	.... 10^0	1
Deci-	....	one-tenth	...... 10^{-1}	.............0.1
Centi-	.....	one-hundredth	.. 10^{-2}	.............0.01
Milli-	.....	one-thousandth	. 10^{-3}	.............0.001
Micro-	....	one-millionth	... 10^{-6}	.............0.000,001
Nano-	.....	one-billionth	... 10^{-9}	.............0.000,000,001

These are the generally used prefixes. There are others which are infrequently encountered. The fundamental units are combined with prefixes to give units of convenient magnitude; thus, three-thousandths of a gram are three milligrams. Two thousand meters are two kilometers.

XXII Descriptive Terms Employed in the Study of Morphological Characteristics of Bacteria.

a. Forms in which bacteria occur

1. *Spherical*. Self-explanatory.
2. *Short rods*. Length not more than three times the diameter.
3. *Long rods*. Length more than three times the diameter.
4. *Filaments*. Threadlike.
5. *Commas*. Bent rods, as a comma.
6. *Short spirals*. Self-explanatory.
7. *Long spirals*. Self-explanatory.
8. *Clostridium*. Spindle-shaped; swollen centrally.
9. *Cuneate*. Wedge-shaped.
10. *Clavate*. Club-shaped.
11. *Vibrio*. Comma-shaped.

b. Groupings in which bacteria occur

1. *Micrococcus*. Spherical bacteria occurring singly.
2. *Bacillus*. Short or long rods occurring singly.
3. *Diplococcus*. Spherical bacteria occurring in pairs.
4. *Tetrads*. Spherical bacteria occurring in groups of four.
5. *Streptococcus*. Spherical bacteria occurring in chains of three or more cells.
6. *Strepto-bacillus*. Rod-shaped bacteria occurring in chains of three or more cells.
7. *Sarcina*. Spherical bacteria occurring in cubical packets.
8. *Staphylococcus*. Spherical bacteria occurring in irregular clusters or masses.

c. Appearance of the ends of bacterial cells

1. *Rounded*. Self-explanatory.
2. *Truncate*. Ends abrupt, square.
3. *Concave*. Ends curved in toward center of cell.
4. *Tapering*. Self-explanatory.

d. Spores (endospores)

1. *Location:* equatorial or central—at center of cell; subterminal—between center and end of cell; terminal—at end of cell.
2. *Shape:* spherical, ellipsoid, or cylindrical.

XXIII Bacteriological Cultures and Common Pathogenic Findings.

Culture	Pathogen
1. Ascitic and Peritoneal Culture	Common pathogen Streptococcus
2. Blood Culture	Common pathogen E. typhosa
3. Bronchial and Pleural Culture	Pneumococcus and M. tuberculosis
4. Joint Culture	Streptococcus of rheumatoid arthritis
5. Pus and Exudate	Staphylococcus
6. Spinal Fluid	Staphylococcus, Streptococcus, Pneumococcus, D. intracellularis
7. Urine	Enteric organisms, Staphylococcus, Streptococcus
8. Anal Culture	Salmonella, Shigella
9. Ear Culture	Staphylococcus, E. Coli, Streptococcus, Pseudomonas
10. Eye Culture	Pseudomonas, Streptococcus, Staphylococcus, Pneumococcus
11. GU Tract	N. gonorrheae, Streptococcus, Streptococcus
12. Mouth and Gum Culture	Vincent's spirochetes, Streptococcus, Staphylococcus
13. Skin Lesion	Fungi, Streptococcus, Staphylococcus
14. Nasopharyngeal	C. diphtheriae, Staphylococcus, Streptococcus
15. Gastric	M. tuberculosis
16. Feces	Salmonella, Shigella
17. Sputum	M. tuberculosis, Staphylococcus, Streptococcus

XXIV Hematology Laboratory Tests:
Purposes, Findings, Instruments and Materials Used.

Test	Purposes, Findings	Instruments, Materials
1. Whole Blood Count	Detect infection, granulocytosis	Hemocytometer, microscope
2. Hematocrit	Volume of packed red cells	High speed centrifuge
3. Hemoglobin	Amount of hematin iron	Spectrophotometer
4. Differential Blood Count	Infection, leukemia, RBC morphology	Differential stain and microscopic enumeration
5. C-Reactive Protein	Infection not detected by blood count	CRP reagent with patient's serum
6. Eosinophil Count	Kidney function with medication	Eosinophil stain and microscope
7. Platelet Count	Hemophilia	Stained smear and microscope
8. Red Cell Count	Red blood cell estimation	Hemocytometer and microscope
9. Sickle Cell	Sickle cell anemia	Special preparation and microscope
10. Rh Typing	Rh factor	Known antiserum and patient's cells
11. ABO Grouping	Blood type	Known antiserum and patient's cells

XXV Urinalysis: Purposes, Findings,
Instruments and Materials Used.

1. Albumen	Kidney function	Combistix
2. Sugar	Diabetes	Combistix
3. pH	Acidity-alkalinity	Combistix
4. Ketone bodies	Diabetic coma	Acetest
5. Specific gravity	Specific gravity	Float
6. Phenolsulfonephthalein (PSP)	Kidney function	PSP dye

XXVI Applications of the Plant Groups in the Social Life of Man.

(A) *Thallophyta* (Algae) can poison water and kill animals which drink it; source of iodine and potash; source of agar-agar (medicine and medium for the cultivation of bacteria); form coral reefs, atolls, and islands; when dried, made into fishing lines and tool handles; used by various animals for food. (Fungi) often destroy food, clothing, and lumber; help in decay of plant and animal remains; mushrooms are used as food, although they are sometimes poisonous; flavor of cheeses, sauerkraut, butter, and vinegar; penicillin; yeast is a fungus; often cause human disease.

(B) *Bryophyta* is used for packing materials in shipping; used in surgical dressings; used in gardening; fuel; source of some chemicals and medicines; change rock into soil; aid in preventing soil waste by erosion.

(C) *Pteridophyta:* Large roots of ferns used as food; used in making perfumes; chemicals (tannin, ethereal oils) for commercial purposes; medicines; some ferns are poisonous; used for scouring and polishing purposes; prevent soil erosion.

(D) *Spermatophyta:* Lumber, pulp wood, pencils; cigar boxes; chests, trunks, and posts; turpentine, spruce gum and oils; Christmas trees; fuels; wood; coal; charcoal; coke (carbone); gas for heating; cooking; petroleum; gasoline; kerosene; cotton; straw; rubber; dyes; foods.

XXVII Applications of the Animal Groups in the Social Life of Man.

(A) *Protozoa:* Chalk, flint, slate, and deep-sea deposits; may give unpleasant odors, tastes, and colors to water; produce human and animal diseases; destroy bacteria; furnish food for other animals; used in laboratory experiments.

(B) *Porifera* furnish protection for both plant and animal organisms; not used for food; frequently attach themselves to water pipes, reservoirs, water filtration equipment, and otherwise interfere with water systems; chalk and flint formations; sponges in commercial use ($2,000,000 annual value).

(C) *Coelenterata:* Food for fish; form coral reefs and islands; jewelry; food for man.

(D) *Platyhelminthes:* When in man and other animals as parasites, they may interfere with digestion and absorption; may cause severe anemia and other disorders in man; used in experiments.

(E) *Nemathelminthes* infest animals; produce some human diseases such as trichinosis, elephantiasis, and hookworm; harm plants; used in experimentation.

(F) *Echinodermata:* Slate pencils; experiments; food for animals and sometimes man; limestone.

(G) *Annelida* are food for higher animals; mix good and bad soils; destroy dead plant materials; used experimentally.

(H) *Mollusca:* Button manufacture; ground for chicken feed; fertilizer; ornaments; road-building processes; window panes in certain parts of the tropics; experiments; food; transmit diseases; attack eggs of fish; destroy plants; host to parasites; cuttle bone (bird food); some inks; octopus sometimes attacks man; bait.

(I) *Arthropoda:* Food for man and other animals; injure dikes, dams, reservoirs by burrowing into them; clean pools and streams; laboratory studies; some attack plants; mites cause itch; "chigger bites"; ticks; carry diseases; some kill insects; poisonous spiders; hog feed; fertilizer; used in tanning animal skins; aid in pollination of plants; bees produce honey; injury to man and other animals, plants and crops; commodities.

(J) *Chordata:* Food; oil and fertilizer; leather goods; clothing; destroy insects and animals; provide sport; skin, hair, hoofs; transportation; labor.

ACKNOWLEDGMENTS

This work would not have been produced without the energetic attention provided by Blanche Johnston, a former member of the biology teaching staff of The Woman's College of Georgia who now teaches at William Woods College in Fulton, Missouri. Professor Johnston gave special help toward development of the contents and organization of the book. She also directed the preparation of certain sections of the manuscript in their formative stages, including the plant and animal outlines and the sections on biological reagents and the assistant's duties.

Appreciation is expressed to Dr. J. S. Asteinza, pathologist with Radford Community Hospital, Radford, Virginia, formerly with the Department of Pathology at Milledgeville State Hospital, Milledgeville, Georgia, and to Walter M. Bowman, Director of Laboratories at Milledgeville State Hospital. The author was privileged to associate with Dr. Asteinza and Mr. Bowman during 1962-1964 in the development of a cooperative college-hospital teaching program in anatomy, physiology, and pathology. This program involved students of The Woman's College of Georgia and professional personnel and facilities of Milledgeville State Hospital.

Gratitude must be expressed to Miss Neina Wansley and to Miss Karen Bowman, biology departmental laboratory assistants, for their help in typing and in developing a logical organization of the book's contents. Mrs. Milton Harrington and Mrs. Wrenn Weston also assisted with typing of the manuscript.

It is not feasible to endeavor to recognize individually the original or secondary sources of various methods and techniques utilized in establishing the purposes of this volume. The author does wish to point up his reliance upon the works of Doctors Alfred Brauer, William C. Beaver, Frank E. D'Amour, Frank R. Blood, David F. Miller, Glenn Blaydes and Paul B. Weisz as significant foundation sources of information. The author referred extensively also to a number of culture leaflets distributed by the Carolina Biological Supply Company.

Thanks are due the W. B. Saunders Company for permission to use Dr. Leslie Brainerd Arey's material which appears as summaries IX, X, and XI in Chapter VII. The General Biological Supply House permitted the listing and description of the Turtox Service Leaflets in Chapter II. Merck and Company approved the use of material appearing as summaries XIII-XIX in Chapter VII. D. C. Heath and Company permitted the use of the McClesky-Christopher outline of the morphological characteristics of bacteria, which appears as item XXII in Chapter VII.

Assistance was received at various times from Mrs. Emogene Dial and Mrs. Martha Reynolds.

Dr. Curtis H. Adams of the Department of Biology at the University of Alabama in Huntsville critically read and evaluated the manuscript.

The author's wife, Glenn, contributed long-suffering patience, faith, and encouragement.

References

Anthony, Catherine Parker. *Anatomy and Physiology Laboratory Manual.* St. Louis: The C. V. Mosby Co., 1946.

Atwood, W. H. *A Concise Laboratory Manual and Atlas for Comparative Anatomy.* Saint Louis: The C. V. Mosby Company, 1949.

Arey, Leslie Brainerd. *Developmental Anatomy.* Philadelphia: W. B. Saunders Company, 1948.

Beaver, William C. *Fundamentals of Biology.* Saint Louis: The C. V. Mosby Company, 1939.

Bergman, H. D., E. A. Hewitt, and W. C. Payne. *Laboratory Manual for Experimental Physiology.* Minneapolis: Burgess Publishing Company, 1948.

Brauer, Alfred. *Laboratory Direction for Histological Techniques.* Minneapolis: Burgess Publishing Company, 1957.

Buffaloe, Neal D., and Richard A. Collins. *Laboratory Manual for Principles of Biology.* Englewood Cliffs, New Jersey: Prentice-Hall, Inc., 1963.

Carolina Biological Supply Company. Series of culture leaflets.

D'Amour, Fred E., and Frank R. Blood. *Manual for Laboratory Work in Mammalian Physiology.* Chicago: The University of Chicago Press, 1954.

Deason, Hilary J. (ed.) *A Guide to Science Reading.* New York: New American Library of World Literature, Inc., 1963.

Dorland, W. A. Newman. *The American Illustrated Medical Dictionary.* Philadelphia: W. B. Saunders Company, 1942.

Glass, Arthur W., and Charles Hamrum. *Anatomy and Physiology Laboratory Manual.* Philadelphia: W. B. Saunders Company, 1953.

Heyneman, Donald. *An Illustrated Laboratory Text in Zoology.* New York: Holt, Rinehart & Winston, Inc., 1962.

Kenoyer, Leslie A., and Henry N. Goddard. *Laboratory Manual for General Biology.* New York: Harper and Brothers, 1937.

Mavor, James W. *Laboratory Exercises in General Biology.* New York: The Macmillan Company, 1947.

McClesky, Charles S. and Warren N. Christopher. *Laboratory Manual and Workbook for Elementary Bacteriology.* Boston: D. C. Heath Company, 1947.

McClung, L. S. *General Bacteriology Laboratory Manual.* Philadelphia: W. B. Saunders Company, 1952.

Miller, David F. and Glenn Blaydes. *Methods and Materials for Teaching Biological Sciences.* New York: McGraw-Hill Book Company, 1962.

Moore, Shirley. *Science Projects Handbook.* Washington, D.C.: Science Service, Inc., and New York: Ballantine Books, Inc., 1960.

Palmquist, Edward M., and Loren C. Petry. *General Botany Laboratory Book.* Philadelphia: W. B. Saunders Company, 1951.

Potter, George Edwin. *Textbook of Zoology.* St. Louis: The C. V. Mosby Company, 1947.

Richardson, John S. *Science Teaching in Secondary Schools.* Englewood Cliffs, New Jersey: Prentice-Hall, Inc., 1957.

Schonberger, Clinton F. *Laboratory Manual of General Biology.* Philadelphia: W. B. Saunders Company, 1962.

Stackpole, Catherine E., and Lutie C. Leavill. *Laboratory Manual and Workbook in Anatomy and Physiology.* New York: The Macmillan Company, 1958.

Steele, Harold C. *Outline and Notes in Human Biology with Laboratory Exercises.* Minneapolis: Burgess Publishing Company, 1957.

Steiner, Erich, Alfred E. Sussman, and Warren H. Wagner, Jr. *Botany Laboratory Manual.* New York: The Dryden Press, Inc., 1957.

Stiles, Karl A. *Laboratory Explorations in General Zoology.* New York: The Macmillan Company, 1949.

Storer, Tracy I. *Laboratory Manual for General Zoology.* New York: McGraw-Hill Book Company, 1951.

Storer, Tracy I., and Robert L. Usinger. *General Zoology.* New York: McGraw-Hill Book Company, 1957.

Strausbaugh, Perry D., and Bernal R. Weimar. *A Manual for the Biology Laboratory.* New York: John Wiley and Sons, Inc., 1938.

Taylor, A. B., and Frederick Sargent II. *Elementary Human Physiology.* Minneapolis: Burgess Publishing Company, 1961.

Tipton, Samuel R., and Helen L. Ward. *A Laboratory Manual for Elementary Physiology.* Minneapolis: Burgess Publishing Company, 1955.

Toney, Ray Ethan. *Instructor's Outline for General Botany.* New York: The Century Company, 1932.

United States Department of Labor. *Occupational Outlook Handbook.* Washington, D.C., 1964.

University of Minnesota. *Experimental Physiology.* Minneapolis: Burgess Publishing Company, 1957.

Walling, Zalia V. *Laboratory Manual for Elementary Physiology.* Saint Louis: The C. V. Mosby Company, 1952.

Weathers, C. L. *Laboratory Directions for General Biology.* New York: John S. Swift Company, Inc., 1946.

Weisz, Paul B. *Laboratory Manual in the Science of Biology.* New York: McGraw-Hill Book Company, 1963.

Weisz, Paul B. *The Science of Biology.* New York: McGraw-Hill Book Company, 1963.

Wilson, Carl, and Walter E. Loomis. *Botany.* New York: Holt, Rinehart and Winston, 1962.

Zim, Herbert, *et al.* "The Golden Nature Guide Series": *Mammals* (1955), *The Southwest* (1955), *Fishes* (1956), *Reptiles and Amphibians* (1956), *Rocks and Minerals* (1957), *Zoology* (1958), and *Fossils* (1962). New York: The Golden Press.